AGRICULTURE

Changing Pressu

Agriculture in Britain:
Changing Pressures and Policies

Edited by

Denis Britton

Emeritus Professor
Department of Agricultural Economics,
Wye College, University of London

C·A·B INTERNATIONAL

C·A·B International
Wallingford
Oxon OX10 8DE
UK

Tel: Wallingford (0491) 32111
Telex: 847964 (COMAGG G)
Telecom Gold/Dialcom: 84: CAU001
Fax: (0491) 33508

British Library Cataloguing in Publication Data
Agriculture in Britain: changing pressures and policies.
    1. Great Britain. Agricultural industries
    I. Britton, Denis
    338.10941

    ISBN 0-85198-655-2

Printed and bound in the UK by BPCC Wheatons, Exeter

Contents

Foreword

As we move into the 1990s, the pace of change seems to be quickening on every side. Political frontiers and blocs are being re-shaped; trading patterns are becoming more fluid as barriers are removed; new technology is opening up ways of using resources at ever-higher levels of productivity; and new perceptions of human values are asserting themselves as concern for the quality of life gathers strength at the expense of reckless exploitation for the sake of short-term benefits.

Agriculture, in Britain and elsewhere, is as much exposed to the impact of these changes as any other part of the economy. The agricultural way of life has already undergone a transformation, and its stability has been shaken. If it is not to be swept along by forces outside its control, the agricultural industry has to prepare itself to face pressures and either withstand them or adapt itself to them.

The first need is to identify these pressures, to understand their causes and to weigh their implications. This book is a welcome contribution to that endeavour. The future may be enveloped in swirling mists, but that makes it all the more necessary for producers and policy-makers alike to be heedful of change, to recognize the important landmarks and to steer a prudent and intelligent course as the years unfold.

Lord Plumb of Coleshill, MEP, DL, Hon.DSc.
Formerly President of the European Parliament and President of the
National Farmers Union.
Honorary Fellow of Wye College, University of London.

Contributors

Denis Britton is Emeritus Professor at Wye College, University of London, having held the chair of Agricultural Economics from 1970 to 1983. He holds honorary doctorates from the universities of Bonn and Padua. From 1979 to 1982 he served as President of the International Association of Agricultural Economists. His publications include *Cereals in the United Kingdom* (1969), (with Berkeley Hill) *Size and Efficiency in Farming* (1975) and (with H. F. Marks) *A Hundred Years of Food and Farming; A Statistical Survey* (1989).

Ruth Gasson read agriculture at Wye College and agricultural economics at Oxford. Later she obtained a Ph.D. at Cambridge. She is now a Senior Research Fellow in the Department of Agricultural Economics, Wye College. Her publications include *The Economics of Part-time Farming* (Longman, 1988).

Berkeley Hill is a member of the Department of Agricultural Economics at Wye College and a consultant to Eurostat on the measurement of incomes in agriculture. He has headed teams on research contracts studying policy issues for MAFF, the Department of the Environment and the European Commission. Recent books include (with D. Ray) *Economics for Agriculture* (Macmillan, 1987); *Total Incomes of Agricultural Households* (Eurostat, 1988); and *Farm Incomes, Wealth and Agricultural Policy* (Gower, 1989).

Ian Hodge, who obtained his Ph.D. degree at Wye College, University of London, is Gilbey Lecturer in the Department of Land Economy, University of Cambridge, where he has specialized in rural development, environmental management and land use. His publications include (with Martin Whitby) *Rural Employment: Trends, Options, Choices* (Methuen, 1981).

Edmund Neville-Rolfe, M.A., Dip.Agric.Econ.(Oxon.), farmed in Wiltshire after the War. During the 1960s he worked at the Agricultural Economics Research Institute in Oxford. He founded the Bureau Européen de Recherches in Brussels in 1973, and was its Director until 1988. Between 1980 and 1987 he was special adviser on European questions to the House of Commons Select Committee on Agriculture. His publications include *The Politics of Agriculture in the European Community* (European Centre for Political Studies, London, 1984).

John North, B.Sc., M.S.(Univ. of California), F.I.Biol., was Chief Agricultural Officer in the Ministry of Agriculture, Fisheries and Food before moving in 1985 to the Department of Land Economy at the University of Cambridge to undertake a research study of the long-term prospects for agricultural production and land use in the United Kingdom. He is a member of the Council of the Royal Agricultural Society of England.

Introduction and Summary

Denis Britton

Agriculture has always been beset by uncertainty. Violent fluctuations in the weather, unpredictable behaviour of market prices, new forms of government interference, the outbreak of crippling diseases and pests – all these have been familiar but unwelcome accompaniments to the steady rhythm of the changing seasons.

In recent times a further source of uncertainty has been added to the list. Farmers now have to encounter a disturbing change in public attitudes to their activities. Criticisms are directed at them from many sides and through many channels. Environmentalists single out various farming activities as being detrimental to the soil, the water supplies, wildlife and the appearance of the countryside, and they seek to impose controls. Consumers are suspicious of the hygienic quality of the foods available to them and they urge the government to introduce more stringent regulations. Animal welfare groups condemn certain forms of livestock production and agitate for their prohibition. Ramblers and motorists protest that access to the fields, footpaths and viewpoints is unnecessarily restricted, and press the claims of recreation against those of production. Developers clamour for the release of more land from agricultural production, which is no longer urgently needed. Taxpayers begrudge the subsidies and other forms of financial protection which farmers and landowners enjoy, and they see no justification for this continuing 'favouritism'.

All these pressures have put farmers on the defensive. Many of them feel that they are misrepresented and misunderstood. They see their job as difficult enough, without this added hostility; and they see the envy of their economic status as being quite unjustified as they contemplate the ceilings placed on their prices and production and their rising burden of indebtedness.

Some of them know that their farms are too small to provide a livelihood, and wonder what else they can do to raise their incomes. They are strongly urged by the government and by various official bodies to 'diversify' their activities, and are responding as best they can.

Nothing in this catalogue of troubles is entirely new. It is their mounting intensity which justifies the widespread assertion that agriculture is in crisis – defined in the dictionary as 'the point in the progress of a disease when an important development or change takes place which is decisive of recovery or death'. Not that anyone is expecting the death of agriculture, but there is growing concern about the prospect of its recovery from its present malaise. If the above definition of crisis is thought to be too pessimistic, readers may prefer the alternative of 'a state of affairs in which a decisive change for better or worse is imminent'.

This book attempts to address the questions: What is happening to British agriculture? and What is likely to happen to it in the next 10–25 years, or beyond?

Contributions were invited from a number of authors, each being a specialist in a particular aspect of agriculture and its relationship with the physical and social environment or with political and economic conditions and institutions. There has been no organized attempt to co-ordinate the findings of the various chapters, or to eliminate possible inconsistencies or overlaps between them. The only common requirement was that the authors should look into the future in the light of the present.

The questions being considered are wide-ranging, and we have to acknowledge that some aspects have been dealt with in very summary fashion, or even totally ignored. In particular we are aware of the need to look at agriculture as being only one part of the complex food chain which ends with the consumer and involves a great many intermediaries and industries, all of which will have an influence on the future development of agriculture as their source of supply. In many respects the farming and food industries have become inseparable. At various points in the book this linkage is acknowledged, but we have not been able to explore it as fully as it deserves. That would require another team of specialists to do it justice.

Chapter 1 identifies some of the main current trends, making use of the available statistical evidence. This is considered to be a worthwhile exercise because some of these trends have been so regular and persistent, over so many years, that it would be foolish not to be mindful of the likelihood and consequences of their continuance. It is not suggested that there is a necessary permanence or inevitability about these trends, nor that trend projections can reliably be used as forecasts. Professor Colin Spedding has reminded us that most trends have the seeds of their destruction built into them. Nevertheless, history shows that these major economic and structural trends have an impressive way of maintaining their direction, and even their pace, in the face of many short-term and unpredictable vicissitudes.

Pride of place in this review is given to the compulsive and surging rise in yield per hectare and per animal. Growth rates of 2 or 3% per annum might not seem to be especially remarkable, but they have had a profound effect on total supplies to a market which does not normally call for such increases.

The most obvious effect has been on producers' prices for farm products, which – after correcting for changes in the value of money – have been showing a persistent tendency to decline at a rate of 4–5% per annum. This has been the root cause of farmers' anxieties, often concealed but always in evidence when the accounts have to be reckoned up.

Falling real prices have exerted a squeeze on farm incomes. Farmers have had the frustration of seeing their total volume of production expand but its real sale value diminish. This sale value in 1988 was only 75% of what it had been in 1974. Such a trend cannot continue without the collapse of a large number of businesses.

The situation of cereal growers is highlighted, and some consideration is given to the options which they may confront: to shift, if they can, to more profitable enterprises; to buy or rent more land; to improve output per £ of inputs on their existing land area; to find supplementary sources of income (which may include 'set-aside' payments); or to give up farming altogether, rather than incur increasing losses.

The continuing tendency for farms to become larger and fewer is observed and analysed. This structural adjustment is to some extent inhibited by rigidities in the land market, but it seems likely that by the year 2000 there may be 25,000 fewer holdings in the UK than at present.

Enterprises (cereals-growing, potato-growing, milk production, etc.) are also becoming larger and fewer. The number of cereal growers in England and Wales fell from 172,000 in 1967 to 87,000 in 1988; potato-growers, from 105,000 to 31,000; and dairy herds from 132,000 to 48,000. The chances of survival have been weighted against the smaller producers, but these have not disappeared altogether.

Of all the trends to be seen in British agriculture, the most persistent has been the decline in the labour force. The period of most rapid reduction was in the 1960s, and the main reason was mechanization. This, coupled with yield improvements, led to a very significant increase in output per person employed. The rate of reduction is now slowing down, and opportunities for further labour-saving on farms have diminished.

Weekly earnings of farm workers have shown a substantial increase, in real terms, from the very low levels which prevailed in the post-war years. The gap between these earnings and the average income of farmers has narrowed, and in this respect the status of the farm worker has shown a marked improvement. He remains, however, at or near the foot of the national wages ladder.

By the year 2000 we might expect to have a total agricultural labour force (hired and family) some 15% smaller than at present, with an increasing preponderance of the family element. Because of the 'diversification' of activities on and around farms, the 'agricultural' labour force will become more difficult to identify, both statistically and socially.

Finally Chapter 1 looks at land ownership and land tenure. In spite of incursions by financial institutions into the land market, most farm land is still owned by private individuals or families. Owner occupation has been on the increase at the expense of tenant farming for nearly 70 years, but in recent years, with high rates of interest and the persistence of relatively high land prices, owner occupiers with large loans to repay and a reduced level of farming profit have found themselves in a very difficult financial situation.

The status of rent-receiving landowners relative both to farmers and farm workers has diminished, and their share in the value of the product of agriculture has been sharply eroded since the so-called Golden Age of farming in 1850–75, when about 20% of the product accrued to land-owners as net rent, compared with only 3% today.

The future pattern of land tenure seems likely to be influenced as much by political as by economic factors. The slogan 'this land is our land' is voiced on both sides of an argument about ultimate rights of ownership. However, as yet there is little sign that a drastic erosion of family inherit-ance, either of land or of other assets, is in prospect, though owners have become noticeably more defensive. In spite of the fall in farming profit-ability, neither inheritance taxes nor the statements of intention about a wealth tax appear to have shaken the belief that farm land is a secure asset. The survival of tenancy in one form or another seems also to be in little doubt.

Chapter 2 considers the changing public attitudes to farmers and farming. It begins with a reminder that during and after the Second World War there was a general positive appreciation of farmers' achievements, and a political consensus about the appropriate direction of agricultural policy. The system of deficiency payments, the cost of which was met by taxpayers, was generally accepted. If, at that time, there was any threat to the quality of the landscape it was perceived as arising from neglect or disuse, not from farmers' methods of production.

The strength of the farmers' position in the public mind began to be undermined after Britain entered the EC in 1973. Consumers' and tax-payers' doubts about the costliness of the Common Agricultural Policy (CAP) coincided with the weakening of the bargaining position of the National Farmers' Union (NFU) as a result of the need for agricultural measures (especially price determination) to be agreed between all Member States.

Soon afterwards, farmers began to come under attack for their allegedly harmful impact on the environment. The health lobby also began to voice criticisms of some of the basic products of British agriculture. Later, a series of specific health scares further dented the farmer's image.

All these and other assaults began to influence government thinking. In 1986 the remit of the Ministry of Agriculture, Fisheries and Food was widened to include concern for the economic and social interest of rural areas, the conservation and enhancement of the natural beauty and amenity of the countryside and the promotion of the enjoyment of the countryside by the public. In 1987 the Minister affirmed that 'a new balance of policies' had to be struck, 'with less support for expanding production'. The NFU made similar changes to its statements of policy objectives. Debate now revolves about the specific ways in which production should be restrained and the environmental impact be mitigated.

The results of several surveys of public opinion relating to the role of farmers in the countryside are quoted. They show that in spite of the widespread view that modern farming damages the countryside, the public by and large continue to have a high regard for farmers and believe that they look after the countryside well. However, they want to see encouragement of more recreation facilities and wildlife, and less regard for food production. Also the public appears to be much more critical of some aspects of livestock production than it was some 15 years ago. Realignment of agricultural policy is thought to be inevitable in view of these changing attitudes, but its extent and exact direction have yet to be determined.

Chapter 3 looks at the prospects for continuing development and application of new technology in agriculture, and its implications. The early adopters of each successive innovation benefit most. Others are then obliged to apply the same technology. This is the 'technological treadmill'.

Many improvements in plant growth are in prospect and their scientific basis is described in detail. Some will take the form of transferring desirable characteristics from one plant variety to another by well-established plant-breeding techniques. Others will come from the rapid advances being made in biotechnology, largely through gene manipulation.

In the control of diseases, pests, frost damage, and losses through respiration, much is expected from the use of biocontrol agents produced through biotechnology.

Improvements in crop management can be expected, following the advance in knowledge of the needs of the crops and also from more accurate monitoring and control so as to ensure optimum timing of operations.

Progress is being made in improving the efficiency of nitrogen-fixing micro-organisms and in establishing new symbiotic associations between them and crop plants.

In animal production, too, the more widespread application of existing technology will continue to ensure increases in productivity, whilst new technology, including multiple ovulation and embryo transplants, should increase the potential rates of improvement substantially.

It is thought that in general the new biotechnology associated with animal production will be available for commercial use earlier than developments in plant production. Tables are given suggesting possible time schedules for the commercial introduction of specific new advances in plant and animal technology.

It is pointed out that farmers need these advances, as the market is becoming more specialized and is demanding specific qualities and greater reliability and continuity of supplies.

Probably the most important finding of Chapter 3 is that higher levels of productivity will result in a surplus of resources relative to needs, so that a new balance in resource use will be inescapable. At the same time, the use of biological rather than chemical technologies could well prove to be of greater environmental significance than any reduction in the quantity of inputs.

New technology may have a direct effect on the size-structure of farms, particularly if the new techniques can be effectively introduced only above a certain 'threshold' size of operation.

The final section of the chapter considers some implications of new technology for specific products, namely cereals, grassland, milk, beef and sheep production and forestry (including farm woodlands).

Chapter 4 will probably be regarded by many readers as being central to the whole book. It deals with questions relating to the future use of Britain's present area of agricultural land, taking into account the expected improvements in technology described in Chapter 3. It comes to the challenging conclusion that some 5 million hectares may have to be diverted to non-food uses or taken out of agriculture altogether.

Agricultural policy will not directly determine future land use patterns. These will be the outcome of individual farmers' decisions taken in response to economic and political constraints and opportunities. The chapter does not envisage 'land use planning' at the national level.

The method used is to present some alternative 'land use budgets' which take account of expected market requirements and the expected productivity of the land when new technology is applied to various land-using enterprises. (The choice of the year 2015 for these forward budgets is explained in Chapter 3.)

Britain's population is not expected to grow by more than about 4% between now and 2015. Other studies have estimated that demand for food at the farm gate per head of population is virtually static, in spite of a growth in income of about 2% per annum. The estimates of total domestic demand used in this chapter take due account of these expected modest rates of growth in the key variables.

Central to the line of argument is the postulation of certain alternative scenarios, or options, which allow for different degrees of intensity in the use of the resources which are applied to the land, and in the arable/pastoral components of the land use pattern. One of these is described as the 'efficient' scenario, in which producers are expected to be striving for the lowest possible costs of production per unit of output. Generally speaking, this means high-yield farming, with no restrictions on the use of fertilizers, sprays or feedingstuffs. Any accompanying environmental or social costs are not taken into account. However, any indication that 'efficient' farming might result in the abandonment of hill farming is ruled out of consideration, because of declared policy regarding depopulation of hill areas.

Other scenarios provide for greater use of grass and forage in milk production (with less cereals per cow); restrictions on the use of nitrogen (maximum 150 kg/ha); and a combination of these two constraints.

The arithmetic of these alternative scenarios in terms of land use, livestock numbers and (in some cases) labour requirements is worked out, on stated assumptions and always keeping in mind the 'ceiling' imposed by total requirements of the domestic market. However, possibilities of import substitution, new agricultural enterprises, exports and the production of industrial raw materials on farms are also reviewed, as they might to some extent keep in production land which would otherwise pass out of use.

The sense of conflict between agricultural and other interests is examined in Chapter 5. Many of the seeds of conflict are to be found in the fact that a great deal of land is not in single but in multiple use, or is in different use from other land in close proximity, thus creating a clash of interests. A table gives illustrations of land uses which give rise to adverse effects on other users and thus create a situation of conflict.

To counteract any impression which may have been given that most people regard farmers as the principal threat to the future of the country-side, a survey is quoted which showed that most people regarded industrial pollution as a greater threat. Even so, there are some bodies, such as the Nature Conservancy Council, which hold farmers responsible for a great deal of damage to ecosystems, amenity values, purity of water supplies and other nuisances. The removal of hedgerows is particularly contentious. The blame is frequently attributed to the enlarged scale and increasing special-ization of farming operations, coupled with profit-maximizing behaviour which demands high levels of application of fertilizers and chemicals. The high price of land has necessitated its intensive use.

A number of groups loosely labelled as 'countryside organizations' comprise an increasingly formidable mass movement of people who are making claims to use land in particular ways which are often more than likely to bring them into conflict with farmers. They give expression to a different set of values, sometimes described as 'post-materialist'.

The structure of communities living in rural areas has changed profoundly, to such an extent that farmers sometimes feel that they are the strangers. The complex composition of a village population is described. Newcomers have a considerable impact on the housing situation, and pressure increases for housing and industrial development.

The question arises: is conflict now inevitable? Is compromise possible, given the recognition of common interests? One possible solution might lie in the segregation of land uses. Yet many countryside values depend on the proximity of agriculture. Conservationists who urge the abandonment of areas of agricultural land may find that they have to reach a compromise.

On the farmers' side, they will be increasingly urged to develop conser-vation values on their farms. They may find that this can be done at relatively little cost, but to the extent that they feel obliged to give first priority to maintaining their income from farming, agricultural funding may have to be redirected towards conservation efforts. However, CAP budgets have not yet moved significantly in that direction.

Chapter 6 takes up the challenging conclusion of Chapter 4 by considering what will happen to the supposed 'surplus' of land. If it is kept in food production by policies of price and income support, this will perpetuate market surpluses.

This leads into a discussion of the 'set-aside' scheme, introduced in 1988 as an EC instrument of policy but proposed by Britain for consideration at the European level some years earlier. Farmers who agree to take land out of arable cropping for at least five years receive annual payments per hectare, on certain conditions. Only a very small proportion of farmers availed themselves of these payments in the first two years of the scheme (see also Chapter 10). The aim of the scheme is to restrict production, but it gives no inducement to enhance nature conservation. An additional Countryside Premium is now available to farmers who undertake positive management of land set-aside for the benefit of wildlife, the landscape, and the local community.

With regard to claims for the release of agricultural land for urban development, it is now officially admitted that 'it no longer makes sense to retain as much land as possible in agricultural use'. Powerful rural voices have protested lest planning controls be relaxed too readily. Environmental as well as agricultural issues are involved. The shift of emphasis in policy is not likely to lead to a free-for-all for developers, but their total land requirements appear small against the incipient surplus foreseen in Chapter 4. The arguments between developers and planners will not be about how much land, but about where it is to be released.

The reduced demand for agricultural land might be expected to lead to the provision of new areas for nature conservation and access; but as yet farmers have no direct incentive to move in this direction. The chapter goes on to consider ways in which policy could be changed for the benefit of the rural environment. The measures relating to designated Environmentally Sensitive Areas (ESAs) provide one possible model. Any restrictions placed on farmers for the benefit of the environment must be based on simple, enforceable criteria.

The promotion of nature conservation, amenity and access values, whether on productive or on 'waste' land, requires management of the land in question. Management agreements and management by major conservation bodies are discussed. There could also be scope for management by local authorities (for the benefit of the local community), and even by a publicly owned Land Bank.

The fashionable concept of 'sustainable development' seems likely to drive the discussion in the next stages of the environmental debate, but its meaning is imprecise. The author calls for a more complete recognition of the costs (long term as well as short term) associated with economic development, rather than a brake on economic development as such.

Future generations would then not be forgotten.

The reference to 'pressures' in the title of this book is taken up in Chapter 7. In agricultural policy-making the erstwhile consensus has evaporated, and more voices demand to be heard. A new range of possibilities has been opened up. At the same time, agricultural matters have invaded high-level politics, because of the prominence of agriculture in the EC budget. The room for manoeuvre at the national level is restricted by the necessity of keeping in step with decisions from Brussels. Neither party doctrine nor public opinion within the UK can dictate the future of British agriculture.

To the surprise of the British, public opinion surveys have shown that in most Member States there is a strong belief that consumers have benefited from the CAP. This must be a source of encouragement to politicians in those countries who do not wish to see the CAP fundamentally changed. The British are often made to feel alone in this respect.

Public opinion exerts a direct influence on farming through its expressions of demand for various kinds of food. A table of consumption trends for major foods shows some perceptible long-term changes. Dietary habits change, especially under the influence of supposedly authoritative recommendations regarding healthy eating. Any major shift from animal products to vegetable products would clearly have important implications for land use; but as yet no such shift appears to be under way.

Choices about what food to buy are influenced not only by nutritional considerations but also by concern for the way in which foods are produced and presented. This is illustrated in the demand for organically produced vegetables and free range eggs. Procurement policies adopted by the large retail companies are already beginning to reflect this concern, and this is bound to have its effects on the farm. However, it may be that the 'green image' is being overdone.

Pressure on farmers from conservationists takes many forms. A prominent concern is with the lowering of pollution, but many seek to go beyond this and to enhance the 'richness of experience' in the countryside. Some want to promote mixed farming; they would encourage tenancy; and they would like to provide more work on the land. Others urge a more humane system of animal production.

European expressions of environmental concern vary from country to country, but a survey conducted by the Commission found that in all countries public opinion regards environmental protection as an urgent problem. This suggests that the public would favour a policy to restrain agricultural production if this could be shown to bring environmental benefits. The diversity of national priorities in this area might work in favour of national discretionary powers in implementing EC policy guidelines.

The chapter then turns to electoral influences. In Britain, with such a small proportion of the population engaged in farming, their voting behaviour is of no great significance. Even in marginal constituencies it is likely that it would be the non-agricultural aspects of rural policy which would swing a sufficient number of voters one way or the other. In all European countries the 'agricultural' vote is declining, though where coalition politics results in precarious majorities, farm interests still exercise a strong influence and receive widespread support which is unrelated to their numbers.

The environmentalist or 'green' vote is a very different matter. It has shown a dramatic upsurge, and cannot be ignored. The pressure it exerts is not necessarily anti-agricultural, but policies which promote greater food output and which threaten the environment will not receive support.

Besides votes, there are lobbies. In the past the farmers' lobby has been particularly successful by becoming incorporated in the policy-making process. Nowadays it has to apply its pressure partly through COPA, the federation of farmers' unions in the EC; but many issues remain to be resolved on a domestic basis. To the extent that the NFU tends to be dominated by large farmers, it can hardly be expected to show much enthusiasm for a policy change in Brussels towards the targeting of support towards small and low income farmers (see also Chapter 8).

Up to now, consumer groups do not appear to have brought much pressure to bear. Environmental groups, on the other hand, have gained strong support from the media and some are heard with increasing attention and respect.

The chapter concludes with the observation that whereas some farmers will respond to all the pressures to which they are subjected by seizing opportunities to satisfy new demands, many will find that the effects on them will be gradual rather than requiring a break with the past.

Chapter 8 underlines the importance of farm incomes in the whole view of the agricultural scene. Many of the changes which can be observed in the appearance and structure of agriculture – the enlargement of farms, the adoption of new technology, the reduction in the hired labour force, specialization, part-time farming – can be explained in terms of the farmer's response to pressure on his income; and until very recently, agricultural policy has been mainly preoccupied with measures to support farm incomes. There is much evidence that the general level of incomes from farming is falling, and that 'the fundamental pressures at work will continue to constrain the income of the agricultural branch of the economy' – as well as tending to make it more unstable from year to year. Yet, at the same time, landowning farmers tend to be found in the wealthiest section of society, and in practice farm income support has meant transferring money from consumers and taxpayers who are, in general, less wealthy than the farmers who are benefiting the most.

In view of this disparity between the wealth of farmers and their incomes, and of the distortions of markets which many agricultural policies (and especially the CAP) have created, a general case for support of farm incomes seems no longer to be accepted, and it may be that in the next 20 years support will be targeted more specifically to those in greatest need of it. Attention would then shift from protecting the size of the 'cake' (the income of the agricultural industry) to ensuring larger slices of the cake to particular groups of farmers.

In that case, much more attention will have to be given to such questions as: who are the 'farmers' to whom the income policy is directed? Should account be taken of the total income of the farm family (including income from investments, pensions and 'outside' work), and not just of the income from farming obtained by the farm operator? Can the necessary information about total personal incomes be obtained? And even the wider question: are farmers such a special case that it is necessary to have an incomes policy for them which does not extend to people in other forms of employment?

The speed with which this change in priorities will be adopted will depend in part on the rate at which the number of farms continues to fall, since this affects the number of slices into which the cake has to be divided, and their average size. Under economic pressures, the minimum viable size of a full-time farm will continue to rise, and some of the small farmers now adjudged to be proper 'targets' of income support measures may no longer be in the 'farmer' category by the time the policy has been re-structured.

Chapter 9 looks more closely at the increasing prevalence of part-time farming, already mentioned in Chapter 8 in the context of incomes policy. The combination of farming with other paid work undertaken by the farmer or by members of the farm household is on the increase.

At least one-third of farm families in Britain are not wholly dependent on farming for their livelihood. Earnings from other sources often exceed farm incomes by a wide margin, and it is evident that only a small number of part-time farming families have unacceptably low levels of income.

The part-time farmer is less likely than the full-timer to add to the production of unwanted surpluses or to pursue farming practices harmful to the environment. He tends to be less concerned than the full-time farmer with making capital investments on his farm or with expanding the size of his enterprises.

Part-time farming permits an influx into rural society of newcomers from non-farming backgrounds. Their arrival is likely to have a much greater impact on rural communities than the more gradual transition to part-time farming by existing full-time farmers. Many of the new entrants continue in other businesses or professional jobs. Motives other than income are required to explain why they are farming. Equally, for former full-time farmers who have become part-timers, profitability is not necessarily the only consideration. Even so, it is economic pressures which are expected to hasten the trend towards part-time farming in the future. It will probably become more difficult to make a living from farming alone.

In Chapter 10 all the matters discussed in previous chapters are reviewed in the context of the European Community, recognizing that Britain can no longer shape its own policies for agriculture, the rural community or the countryside without reference to this European framework of international agreement and legislation.

The chapter first gives an outline of the main reasons why negotiations for Britain's entry into the Community were so prolonged and difficult, especially regarding trade with Commonwealth countries, Britain's contribution to the EC budget and the requirement to abandon some of the safeguards previously given to British farmers. Some of these bones of contention have remained on the agenda, in one form or another, but Britain was henceforth committed to a reversal of its traditional policies for trade in foodstuffs, market pricing and support measures for farmers.

The operation of 'green' exchange rates for trade in the principal agricultural products within the Community is explained. They have enabled Britain to retain some freedom of action within the CAP framework. More important, however, is the suggestion that recent changes of direction in the CAP, notably the gradual shift in emphasis away from market price support alone to structural measures, will somewhat extend the scope for national initiatives.

The chapter goes on to discuss the significance for Britain of the three pillars of the CAP – Community preference, common prices, and common financing.

The final section deals with some current issues. It is suggested that the planned completion of a single internal market throughout the Community should prove advantageous for British agriculture, with its relatively sound farming structure giving greater scope for innovations in husbandry and marketing. The ability of milk producers to maintain gross margins in the face of quotas has provided one example.

For the European Community, the survival of farmers in a less accommodating economic and political climate will be largely a regional problem, but since all Member States will be affected, common measures will have to be found, and national governments will be required to contribute to their cost. As the structural measures are less rigidly and uniformly enforced than the market regulations, Britain will enjoy some freedom of choice in the way in which the structural measures are applied. However, there will be further positive discrimination in favour of the poorest rural areas of the Community. Any Community system of direct income aids will be designed essentially to help those farmers least well endowed with resources of land and capital.

In the light of comments made in Chapter 8 about the 'targeting' of farm income support, it is interesting to find in this chapter on the EC the suggestion that definition of the dividing line between farmers needing direct income support and those who can manage without it is likely to be left largely to the discretion of Member States.

In regard to the protection of the environment, it seems likely that the

British government will be obliged, in certain areas such as water pollution, to take control measures similar to those already being applied in other Member States. Increased preoccupation of Member States with food quality and safety is bound to lead to an extension of Community legislation in this field. More generally, it is thought that the reduced influence of producers' views on policy will persist for the foreseeable future.

Finally, a section headed Conclusions attempts to identify the adjustments in policy which appear to be needed, once it is accepted that there is now surplus productive capacity in agriculture and that this situation is more likely to be aggravated than otherwise by future technological advances. Provision should be made to deal creatively with the expectation of a continuing shrinkage in the number of full-time farmers. The section ends with a list of some of the questions which have to be put on the agenda for discussion at all levels – local, national and international. Before too long, the discussion period should give way to attempts to reach an informed consensus.

Chapter 1
Recent Changes and Current Trends

Denis Britton

Introduction

Any attempt to look into the future must begin with an appreciation of where we are now, and of how we arrived here. This chapter reviews the main features of British agriculture today and looks for the main trends which have prevailed over the past 20 or 30 years, as revealed by the available statistics. (Burrell *et al.*, 1987; Marks and Britton, 1989; Peters, 1988). Later chapters will consider some of the reasons for these trends and some of their consequences, qualitative and quantitative.

We are well aware that an uncritical acceptance of current trends as a reliable guide to the future could lead to erroneous and even absurd conclusions. So many changes in attitudes, objectives and patterns of living are now taking place that agriculture must undoubtedly be regarded as being in an acute state of flux. Yet in many respects it has seemed so for the past 50 years at least. The fact remains that some of the main trends have been so persistent and of such long duration that it would be equally foolish to disregard them, as though the next page of history will bear no sequential relationship to the last at all.

The following aspects have been selected for review in this chapter, as being both capable of numerical assessment and of special significance for the future of farming: yields, prices, agricultural output and income, size of farms and size of enterprises, employment, and landownership and tenure.

These aspects will recur in various contexts in subsequent chapters. Others are excluded here because of their fuller treatment later, notably the influence of the Common Agricultural Policy (CAP) on British farming and the growing prevalence of part-time farming and pluriactivity of farm households. Yet others would qualify for inclusion if time and space permitted. The changing patterns and forces in international trade, trends in the food processing industries, the food marketing chain and farmer/retailer/consumer relationships, changing dietary preferences and food consumption patterns – all these and many other aspects will undoubtedly play their part in shaping the future but have been outside the range of our close scrutiny.

1

Yields

Yields (production per hectare or per animal per year) will be discussed first, in the belief that the story which they tell lies at the very heart of recent developments in agriculture as a whole. They have permeated the whole structure of the industry. They are a measure of its vitality, and their accelerating advance has been characteristic of agriculture in nearly all developed countries. They challenge the accuracy of the label too readily attached to agriculture as being 'a declining industry'. They seem to have their own momentum which has been remarkably insensitive to changes in national or international policies or market situations, having its source in technical rather than political or economic causes. They have been largely responsible for precipitating some of the crises which farmers have had to face in the form of market instability and depression of incomes – an aspect which will be returned to when looking at price trends later in this chapter.

At the most general level, the yield story is epitomized by the fact that an ever-increasing amount of production has been forthcoming from a constant or declining area of agricultural land. One consequence of this has been that the UK is now more self-sufficient in its food supplies than it was when yields were at a much lower level.

Improvements in yields per hectare or per animal can be shown to be highly correlated with changes in the national agricultural output, but because output is also affected by crop areas and by livestock numbers, yields have their own story to tell.

This review of yields concentrates mainly on two products, cereals and milk. These have been especially significant in their influence on recent agricultural developments, not only because of the persistence and strength of their trends but also because of the important share which they contribute to the total of agricultural production in the UK (about 40%).

Cereals

Before 1939 the average yields of cereals stood at little more than 2 tonnes/ha and had shown hardly any improvement since official records began in the 1880s. There was some increase in the years of World War II, but this was modest compared with the 'take-off' which occurred after 1950, as a result of greater use of fertilizers, adoption of higher-yielding varieties and improvements in weed control (Figure 1.1). Wheat led the way with a well-sustained average annual increase amounting to 2.6% per annum over the period 1952–86. Barley, which was the crop most frequently found suitable for growing on the 600,000 ha of additional land brought into cereals production between 1950 and 1980, achieved a rate of increase in yield (2.0% per annum) which did not quite match that of wheat but nevertheless made a significant contribution to the expansion of

Figure 1.1. Yields of wheat and barley in Great Britain (with exponential and linear projections).

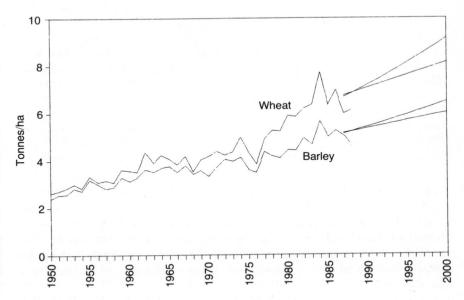

total agricultural output during that period. Oats has generally kept pace with barley, but has dwindled in importance as the area grown has diminished dramatically.

After the record harvest of 1984 yields of wheat and barley have fallen away, but not to levels appreciably below those implied by the long-term trends, and it would be rash to conclude that the underlying momentum has now begun to weaken. It is worth recalling that a somewhat similar lull occurred towards the end of the 1960s, and some commentators at that time expressed with some alarm the view that the upward surge in yields had spent its force, disease was taking its toll and Nature was beginning to impose limits on farmers' ambitions. Four tonnes per ha was thought to be the probable limit to the national average for wheat; yet in less than 20 years after that time the average had reached nearly 8 tonnes.

The technical factors underlying these yield increases are examined in Chapter 3, which also discusses the likelihood of further improvements which may be forthcoming as a result of current and future research and development. At this point it will suffice to note that the yields shown in Table 1.1 would be reached in the year 2000 if the established trends were to continue. (Exponential trends assume constant annual percentage increases; linear trends assume constant annual increments.)

By comparison with cereals, the root crops (potatoes and sugar beet) have shown slower tendencies for yields to increase. Table 1.2 shows a

Table 1.1 Projection of trends for cereals and root crops (tonnes/ha).

	Trend yield 1988	Projected yield year 2000	
		Exponential	Linear
Wheat	6.85	9.18	8.14
Barley	5.22	6.49	6.02
Oats	5.07	6.58	5.94
Potatoes (maincrop)	38.7	49.4	45.2
Sugar beet	40.1	44.6	43.7

long-term trend increase of 1.9% per annum for potatoes and 1.1% for sugar beet. It is noticeable that the rate of increase for sugar beet was much slower in the second half of the period under review. This reflects the disease problems with which sugar beet growers have had to contend.

Table 1.2 summarizes the annual rates of increase in yields in the crops already mentioned, in two successive 17-year periods and in the whole period from 1952 to 1986.

In the absence of a *general index of crop yields* in the official statistics, such an index has been calculated for inclusion here. The separate indices of the annual yields of the five major crops (wheat, barley, oats, potatoes and sugar beet) have been weighted by their respective areas in Great Britain to produce a combined index (Figure 1.2). The graph indicates that by the year 2000, if the exponential trend continues, yields will have risen to three times their 1950 level (or 2.6 times if we follow a linear trend).

Farmers have been warned by the British government and by the European Commission that market requirements for their crops cannot be expected to develop in line with a trend of that kind, so it has important implications for land use. These are considered in Chapter 4.

Milk

Milk is the most important single product in British agriculture, contributing 20% of the value of the national agricultural and horticultural output. Developments in the dairy sector have a strong influence on the general farming prosperity or depression. The key position of milk became particularly evident in 1984 when quotas were first imposed by the European Community. The power of the Community to limit activities on British farms was not fully appreciated by many farmers until this major product was brought under control.

Productivity in the dairy sector depends on several elements. The

Table 1.2 Annual rates of increase in yields per ha, Great Britain.

	Percentage increase		
	1952–1969	1969–1986	1952–1986
Wheat	2.2	2.9	2.6
Barley	1.9	2.1	2.0
Oats	2.3	2.0	2.1
Three cereals	2.1	2.4	2.3
Potatoes (maincrop)	1.7	2.1	1.9
Sugar beet	1.6	0.7	1.1
Two root crops	1.6	1.6	1.6
Five crops	2.0	2.4	2.2

Based on five-year moving averages of annual data.

Figure 1.2. General index of crop yields in Great Britain (three cereal and two root crops. Index:1950=100).

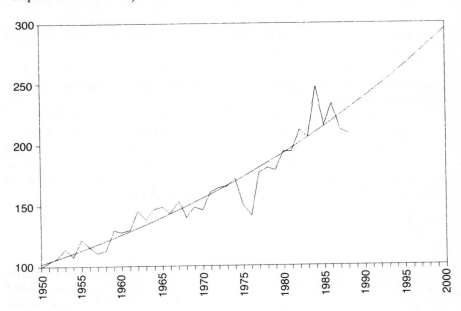

efficient use of grassland, which largely determines the number of cows carried per hectare, mechanization and improved layout in cowsheds, which increases the number of cows which can be milked by one person, the control of disease, and improvements in the quality of purchased feedingstuffs and in their efficient use have all been highlighted in many studies of the economics of milk production. The greatest attention, however, has been focused on the achievement of higher yields of milk per cow.

Studies show that although high yield is no guarantee of high profit margin it is this, more than any other single factor, which has enabled dairy farmers to maintain their incomes in the face of falling real prices paid for milk.

The increase in average yield per cow has been one of the most stable and persistent trends to be observed in British agriculture in the past 50 years (Figure 1.3). Before 1939 there had been little evidence of any regular improvement in yields. An enquiry made in 1925 had shown that average yields then stood at about 2,130 litres, which was thought to have been 'about the same' as in 1908, when a similar enquiry had taken place.

It was not until after 1943 that significant and sustained annual improvements began to be registered in a reliable way. Figure 1.3 shows that yields rose more or less in a straight line between 1950 and 1970, with annual increments of about 60 litres per cow, but that between 1970 and 1982 the pace of change accelerated, giving annual increments of about 100 litres.

After 1982–83 the upward movement in yields came to a halt. Indeed, in the next two years yields suffered a setback greater than any recorded in this country since 1940, when there was a sudden severe shortage of

Figure 1.3. Average yield of milk per cow in England and Wales (with exponential and linear projections).

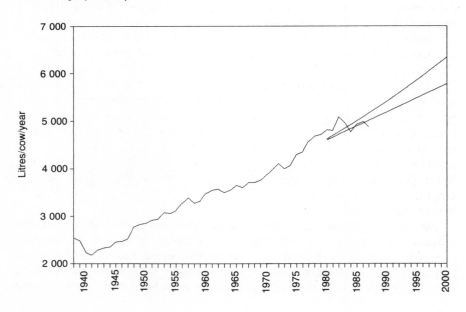

concentrates. No doubt this recent decline was due in part to the uncertainty surrounding dairy farming after the introduction of milk quotas in April 1984. It also seems likely that some producers made special efforts in 1982 and 1983 to maximize yields, so as to establish a strong contingent basis for quota allocation, after which they reverted to more normal levels of concentrate feeding. Certainly expenditure on feedingstuffs was sharply reduced in 1984 and 1985.

It remains to be seen whether or not the long-term upward movement in yields will soon be resumed. Although there is no prospect of any significant expansion in the market requirements in the UK or in Europe, there are reasons to think that a stable volume of production may come from fewer cows with higher yields per cow.

First, there is an accumulation of evidence from many sources, extending to many countries and going back for many years, to show that there is a very strong positive connection between yields per cow and the profitability of the milk enterprise. Other factors, such as changes in prices of feedingstuffs and diminishing physical returns to higher levels of feeding, can and do cut across this relationship, but its underlying influence remains strong. From recent surveys made by the Milk Marketing Board (MMB), covering more than a quarter of a million cows in all regions, it can be deduced that raising yields by 10% would be associated with an increase of over £60 in margin over purchased feed and concentrates per cow. This being so, if production has to be held at present or even reduced levels, it is likely to prove more profitable, within the national quota, to keep fewer cows and raise their average yields than to maintain cow numbers but adjust feeding practices to give lower yields. Cow numbers in the UK in 1988 were 13% below those of 1983, and the number of herds fell by about 10,000 in the same period.

Second, further improvements in breeding techniques, disease control and feeding patterns are on the way and these will raise yield potential (see Chapter 3).

Third, there is no reason to suppose that biological factors will impose a ceiling on average yields at or near the level of 5,000 litres per cow per year, which is the peak yield reached up to now in the total dairy herd of England and Wales. In Denmark, for instance, this level has already been exceeded by at least 14%, the average yield in 1986 being over 5,700 litres per cow per year, and the trend in that country is still strongly upward. Many British dairy farmers have already reached that level: 24% of the cows in the MMB's Milkminder sample in 1987–88 were in herds whose average yields exceeded 6,000 litres.

In the light of these considerations the projections for the year 2000 indicated in Figure 1.3 do not seem to be beyond the bounds of possibility.

Prices

The fact that the raising of agricultural yields has been a universal phenomenon throughout the trading countries has meant that its positive achievements have been blighted for farmers by the constant downward pressure
exerted on prices. The more abundant supplies have meant that market
requirements have been more easily satisfied.

Some producers have sought comfort in the belief that the rising tide of
world population would ensure a market for all the food that could be
produced. They have not realized the melancholy situation that the hungry
millions are virtually without purchasing power and cannot make their
presence felt in the world's agricultural markets.

Meanwhile in the more affluent countries there has been only a small
increase in population, and the demand for food products in their
unprocessed form has remained highly inelastic. Consumers have shown
resistance to any idea that they would readily take up whatever quantities
the farmers had to offer. The simple proposition that the greater the
supply, the lower the price has been demonstrated to be indestructible – a
rock which has been ever-present, even if concealed from time to time by
market turbulence and by policies inspired by national or regional
isolationism.

Inflation has often had the effect of concealing from farmers – and
from consumers too – the reality of the decline in prices of agricultural
products. Those who remember the days when wheat was sold in British
markets for less than £10 a tonne – as it was just before World War II – are
naturally inclined to think that today's prices of £100 to £120 a tonne *must*
represent a substantial improvement compared with the 'bad old days'.
They forget that the pound of 1939 was worth at least 20 times the
pound of today. The price of a tonne of wheat has a much reduced
purchasing power over other goods and services compared with the time
when a yield of 1 tonne per acre (2.5 tonnes/ha) was considered quite
respectable.

During the 1960s, farmers' prices (including the deficiency payments
from the government to compensate for inadequate market prices) were
changed little from year to year. There was a small movement upwards, but
the benefits of this were eroded by the steady advance of inflation, which
was to become rampant in the 1970s and early 1980s. In real terms,
farmers' prices fell by one-third between the post-war heights reached in
1955 and the pre-crisis year, 1972 (Figure 1.4). Most producers responded
to this by looking for ways in which yields could be pushed to still higher
levels. So increased production and falling prices can be seen as the
positive and negative aspects of the same basic cause – the persistence of
the agricultural revolution in terms of technical change.

The world economic crisis of 1973 greatly relieved the downward
pressure on agricultural prices. For a time it seemed as though the days of

Figure 1.4. Producers' prices of agricultural products (indices of current and real values. 1986=100).

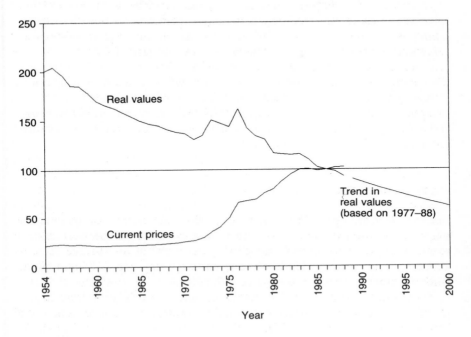

world market surpluses might be over. Fuel prices were very high, fertilizers were in extremely short supply and gloomy forecasts were being made about the rapid exhaustion of the world's productive resources. In current money values, British agricultural prices doubled in four years (1972–76), and even in real terms they rose by nearly 20% in that period – which also coincided with Britain's entry into the European Economic Community, an event which in itself resulted in some upward movement in farm prices during the 'transition' to the Community's higher price regime, though at the time this was of less significance than the world-wide upheaval. On top of all this there occurred the exceptionally adverse weather for potato growers in 1975 and 1976, which cut their output by a third and sent market prices sky-high – up to about seven times the normal level.

The combined effect of all these factors was that the long-term downward trend in real prices was interrupted for a period of about five years (1973–77 inclusive). Farming enjoyed a relatively prosperous period; capital investment and real land values rose to record high levels.

However, it is clear from Figure 1.4 that for the past ten years (1978–88) the downward trend in real prices received by producers has been resumed, even at a faster rate than before, and the period 1973–77 now has the appearance of a temporary aberration – an escape from the tightening grip of the long-term market forces as they respond to the successive waves of technological change.

Expressing the long-term changes in statistical terms, it can be said that since 1954 producers' real prices (after adjustment for inflation) have been falling at an average annual rate of 1.9%. Since the peak of prices was reached in 1976, the decline has been at an annual rate of 4.4%.

Some relief has been afforded by the fact that prices paid by farmers for goods and services used in production have also fallen in real terms, though not so rapidly as farmers' product prices. If allowance is made for this relief, what is called the net price effect (see Eurostat, Rapid Reports, Agriculture) in the same recent period has shown an average downward movement of 3.1% per annum.

Agricultural output and income

For the 30 years up to 1974 the trend in the total volume of agricultural output (field crops, livestock products and horticultural products taken together at constant prices) was steadily upwards, at an average rate of about 2.5% per annum. There was a temporary relapse in 1975 and 1976, when weather conditions were exceptionally adverse, but after that the upward trend continued much as before, until 1984 (Figure 1.5). In the past few years total output has remained fairly steady, at a level somewhat below the peak reached in 1984.

Whether that peak will be acknowledged in the future as an 'all-time high' remains to be seen. 1984 is often described as a watershed for agriculture, being the year in which the agricultural ministers of the Member States of the European Community began to take resolute steps to keep tighter control over the budgetary cost of the Common Agricultural Policy; but good harvests in the next few years could send the total output up to record levels once again.

The long-term achievement, which amounts to a doubling of output in 30 years from a somewhat reduced land area and a much more reduced labour force, has been a matter of pride. It has also brought the nation to a much higher level of self-sufficiency in food supplies – an aim to which more than one generation of politicians has attached great importance, but which may not loom so large in the future.

What is a matter of much greater concern to farmers today is that for the past 20 years, apart from a sudden brief period of unprecedented prosperity in 1973–76, the expansion of output has not resulted in any increase in its total sale value in real terms, but quite the reverse. Because of the price trends described in the previous section, the real value of output has sagged, and in 1988 it stood at 25% below the level of 1974 (Figure 1.5). (The divergence between volume and value of output is reviewed more fully, and over a longer period, in Chapter 8.)

Figure 1.5. Indices of agricultural output and real farming income.+—+—, real value of output; □—□, real farming income;×—×, volume of output.

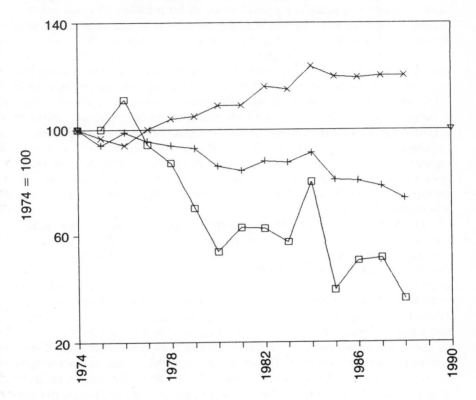

This drastic lopping of rewards for sustained efforts is a course of events which is naturally felt by farmers to be unjust. As many people, including the Duke of Edinburgh in his Dimbleby Lecture, have observed, farmers have been the victims of their own success. If this is what 'submission to the discipline of the market-place' is going to mean for them in the years to come, it is no surprise and no exaggeration if the situation is described as a crisis; it is evident that this trend in the real value of farmers' total receipts from the sale of their output is one which cannot continue without the collapse of a large number of businesses. The impact would not be confined to small farmers, though they would probably bear the brunt, for reasons which we shall consider in a later section.

The effect on the net incomes of farmers (after taking into account their expenditure on feedingstuffs, fertilizers and other supplies and services used in production, as well as machinery, labour, rent and interest) has been even more severe, as Figure 1.5 shows. In general, the prices and costs of these items have risen at a steeper rate than the current prices of farm products. Higher wages for farm workers, higher charges for repair and maintenance of machinery and buildings and higher rates of interest on borrowed capital have all contributed to a sharp reduction in the farmers' residual share in the dwindling real value of output. The average rate of decline in real net farm income (i.e. the national total accruing to farmers as a group) between 1974 and 1988 has been at 7% per annum.

It cannot be said that farmers have brought this upon themselves by making a more lavish use of purchased inputs. Indeed, the volume of inputs has risen at a much slower rate than the volume of final output (0.4 and 2.1% respectively per annum), indicating some continued improvement in the efficiency of resource use. Nor is the situation much relieved by the fact that the national farm income is year by year being shared between a declining number of recipients. Some reduction has been recorded in the number of farmers, partners and directors, but it does not amount to more than 1% a year, while the size of the 'cake' falls by 7% on average, as already indicated. Table 1.3 summarizes the principal factors which have influenced farm income trends.

The severity of the downward pressure on farmers' incomes which has been exerted by falling real prices of farm products and rising costs is strikingly illustrated by Figure 1.6. This shows the typical situation of 'Specialist Cereals' farms in England, that is, farms where cereals account for over two-thirds of the farm output, and it is based on accounts collected from farmers voluntarily under the Farm Business Survey (358 farms in 1980 and 282 farms in 1986). For 1980 the average of the two accounting years 1979/80 and 1980/81 has been used, and similarly for 1986.

Line AA shows the average level of net farm income obtained in 1980 at various levels of farm size. For example, on farms of 100 ha an average net farm income of £10,000 was obtained; at 200 ha the corresponding level of income was about £24,000. These amounts are given in terms of 1986 money values, i.e. allowing for the higher purchasing power of the pound in 1980 compared with 1986.

Line BB shows the situation in 1986 on farms of the same type. The vertical difference between AA and BB represents the reduction in real net income experienced between 1980 and 1986. It reflects the sharp fall in the real prices received by farmers for cereals during this period. Wheat prices fell by 26% and barley prices by 25%, in real terms. As this was not matched by a corresponding fall in prices paid by farmers for fertilizers, sprays, seed, machinery, labour or borrowed capital, it meant that despite the achievement of higher yields of grain per ha and some significant labour-saving changes and other improvements in farming practices (i.e. rising output per unit of input), profitability was sharply reduced.

On farms of 100 ha, real net farm income was halved (from £10,000 to £5,000), and on farms of 50 ha it fell to zero. It should be kept in mind that there are always very wide variations between farms at any given level of size. Some did much better than the average lines in the graph suggest, but a similar number did much worse.

Figure 1.6. The fall in incomes of specialist cereal farms, 1980–1986 in 1986 money values.

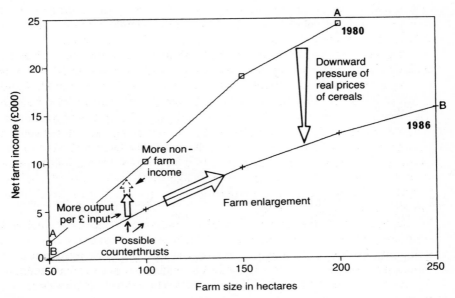

In the light of these figures it is not surprising that Michael Murphy wrote in his Cambridge University Report on Farming in the Eastern Counties of England in 1983/84 that 'the plight of small [cereals] farms less than 40 hectares is now extremely serious'. This was a specific example of what is commonly described, especially in French-speaking countries, as the 'marginalization' of the small farm and its people.

The illustration given relates to a situation which is not unique to producers of cereals. Similar, if less calamitous, illustrations could be given for other crops and for livestock enterprises.

We might pause in our review of recent trends, to consider what farmers could do in the face of such a situation. If they had a clear perception of the outlook for prices (which are, of course, quite outside their control), even the optimists among them could hardly convince themselves that if they did nothing but hold on for another year or two, the situation would improve. There would appear to be at least five other possibilities which they might contemplate:

1. To adapt the pattern of farming, so far as technical and personal conditions permit, shifting to enterprises which are more profitable. If any are to be found, their introduction is likely to involve intensification, investment in buildings and stock (in the case of livestock enterprises), labour problems, and, if pursued by others in a similar situation, further aggravation of the supply/demand situation of these other enterprises.

Table 1.3 Some factors which have affected farm incomes.

Income-raising tendencies

Description	Examples
1. Reduced man-hours in work-performance.	Labour-hours per ha for ploughing and cultivations were reduced by about 30% between 1976 and 1988. Time for silage-making reduced by about 40% in same period. Labour-hours per dairy cow were reduced by about 20% between 1980 and 1985.
2. Higher yields per ha and per animal without proportionate increase in inputs (labour, machinery, feedingstuffs, etc.)	Average wheat yields rose from about 4.4 tonnes/ha in the 1970s to 6.4 in the 1980s.
3. Specialization on fewer but larger enterprises per farm.	Number of registered milk producers fell by 50% between 1970 and 1982, while average size of herd doubled.
4. Enlargement of farms, mainly by taking over land from uneconomic holdings.	Farms of over 300 acres occupied 30% of the total farmland area in 1962, but 46% in 1982 (Eng. & Wales).
5. Intensification on existing area: higher stocking densities.	Specialist dairy farms increased their number of cows per ha by 35% between 1967 and 1980.
6. Increase in certain kinds of government grants.	Premium payments on ewes were introduced in 1981/82 and reached £144 million in 1987/88.
7. More income from non-farming activities.	

Income-lowering tendencies

Description	Examples
8. General fall in prices of farm products (in real terms).	Fall of 32% between 1977 and 1987.
9. Prices of goods and services bought by farmers rising relative to product prices – the farmers' adverse terms of trade.	Ratio of the two indices moved adversely by 30% between 1976 and 1986. Real wages of farm workers rose by 23% between 1977 and 1986.

Table 1.3 continued

10. Reduction or ending of certain kinds of government grants.	Payments under the Agriculture and Horticulture Development Scheme and the Agriculture and Horticulture Grant Scheme fell from £190 million in 1980/81 to £45 million in 1987/88.
11. Higher rents.	Rise of 31% in real terms between 1980 and 1986.
12. Higher rates of interest.	Rates on bank advances rose from 8% in 1972 to 19% in 1980 (but declined thereafter).

2. To contrive to buy or rent some more land in the neighbourhood of the existing farm. In that case, in terms of Figure 1.6 they could reasonably expect to move up the line BB, to the right of their present position. This assumes, of course, that they would be able to farm the additional land nearly as profitably per ha as their existing land; this in turn would depend on the price of the land in relation to its productive capacity and the prospects of being able to use the farm's resources of machinery and labour more economically on the larger area. If these considerations were favourable, the farm of (say) 100 ha, by enlarging to 150 ha, might expect almost to double the net farm income, from about £5,000 to something approaching £10,000. This is the 'solution', coupled with **5** below, which must have been largely responsible for the structural changes described in another section of this chapter.

3. To improve the output per £ of inputs on the existing farm area, i.e. reducing the cost per tonne. If by improvements of this kind (whether output-increasing or input-reducing) the level of performance could be lifted from 'average' to the 'top 10%', the farmer might well succeed in doubling his net income, so wide is the range of performance found in practice. However, if his neighbours and competitors, many of them in the same predicament, have the same attitude as his, and in particular if they all strive for higher yields, the action is likely to be largely self-defeating because it will worsen the market situation.

4. To carry on more or less as at present, but also find supplementary sources of income from non-farming activity, undertaken by the farmer or by one or more members of the family. It is clear that many operators of small farms have been taking this course (see Chapters 8 and 9).

5. To give up farming altogether, selling or renting out all or most of the existing farmland area, but perhaps retaining the use of the house. Another section of this chapter describes the long-term decline in the number of agricultural holdings, which is directly related to, if not an exact reflection of, decisions to quit.

Size of farms and size of enterprises

This section will consider trends in the size of farms, and also in the size of individual enterprises within the farm business. In both aspects significant trends are to be observed.

Size of farms

The size of farms is usually measured in terms of area – either the area under crops and grass or the total area, including rough grazings and some-times woodlands and all other land coming within the farm's boundaries. For most purposes, changes in the size-structure can be adequately described in these terms, and the figures are examined in some detail below.

However, although area is the most readily available measure, it is not always a satisfactory indicator of size. Because of the great variations in intensity of land use, a farm which is relatively small in area can be very large in terms of value of output and vice versa. For this reason, a number of other measures of 'economic size' have come increasingly into use in recent years. These take into account the crops and livestock recorded on the farm, at the time of the agricultural census, and on that basis may refer to the standard labour requirements of the farm as a whole, or to its 'standard gross margin' (SGM), which is a calculation of the expected annual receipts (using regional standard yields and prices of some reference period) minus the operating costs associated with the various products (variable costs).

SGM is now used by the European Community as the recognized measure of economic size. It is expressed in European Size Units (ESU). Until 1983 one ESU corresponded to 1,000 European Currency Unit (ECU); in 1985 its value was set at 1,100 ECU; and further adjustments will be made to take account of changes in agricultural conditions and in the value of money. In the UK a British Size Unit (BSU) has been adopted which in 1987 was equivalent to 2,000 ECU of standard gross margin.

The threshold of 4 BSU is judged by the MAFF to be the minimum below which a farm cannot be regarded as a full-time farm. In 1988 there were 142,000 holdings in the UK above that minimum. This number has been falling since 1983 (when this measurement was introduced) at a rate of about 1,500 a year – a trend which is confirmed by the falling numbers of persons who describe themselves as 'whole-time farmers, partners or directors' in the annual agricultural census.

Whatever measures are used, the dominant feature is that farms have been becoming fewer and larger for a period of about 50 years. The cause is not easy to pinpoint, but the trend has been closely associated with that in mechanization. The replacement of horses by tractors, of horse-drawn reapers and binders by self-propelled combine-harvesters, of potato diggers and their accompanying gangs of pickers by harvesting machines which perform the whole operation, of hand-milking by machine-milking – all these have had the effect of enabling one person to carry out a range of operations on a much larger area than was previously possible.

There was consequently a strong incentive to farmers to raise the land/man ratio; if they could not do this they were likely to be put out of business by others, who might be in their neighbourhood but were just as likely to be thousands of miles away.

There were two possible responses to this challenge – to employ fewer workers while maintaining the farm's output; or to take on more land. The distribution of emphasis between these courses of action would vary from farm to farm. In many cases, one or two agricultural workers were found to be no longer needed, and had to find other employment. Many thousands left agriculture, especially between 1950 and 1970 (see p. 25). In the UK the number of workers fell by nearly half a million during that period. This is not to say that the whole of this reduction had to be brought about by dismissal; the rate of new recruitment was also sharply reduced. Quite often loyal workers were kept on by their employers until the time came for retirement, and then were not replaced.

Farmers who were able to find ways of enlarging their land area, whether by purchase or by renting, could only do so at the expense of other farms, as there was no new land to be brought into cultivation. The only exception to this general requirement of an agreed transfer of land was to be found in the form of conversion of rough grazing land into managed pastures, which in some areas provided very occasional opportunities for effective enlargement of farming operations.

Usually, enlargement took place only when a neighbouring farm fell vacant or when a neighbour was willing to dispose of part of his land and operate at a reduced level of effort and output. It is often forgotten that farm enlargement is a two-way process in which would-be expanders have to succeed in bringing about mutually acceptable arrangements with neighbours who may have to be persuaded or induced to change their way of life.

This process of mutual adjustment is hampered by the lack of fluidity in the land market. The transfer of land from one occupier to another is closely linked with changing family circumstances, especially those brought about by death and succession. This makes the land market a very difficult field of operation for farm business decision-making, compared with the other markets with which farmers are involved, such as commodity markets or the markets for supplies of feedingstuffs, fertilizers and machinery, in which sales and purchases can be quickly negotiated and in which the quantities and delivery dates can be arranged almost at will.

It is possible to imagine a highly adaptable land market, including unlimited and easily negotiated renting arrangements, in the context of which a farmer could expand or contract his land area at any time, so long as he was prepared to pay the going price; but that imaginary situation is a long way from present realities and will remain so, given the hard-won provisions for security of tenure for the present occupiers.

However, in spite of the rigidities of the land market and its 'narrowness' in the sense that at any given time only a very small proportion of the total area of farm land can be considered to be in any way 'available' for occupation if terms can be agreed, there is evidence enough that the pattern of occupation does indeed undergo perceptible changes from year to year, and that in some periods the pace of change has been such as to effect a rapid transformation of the familiar scene.

The changing structure of agriculture in England and Wales is shown in Figure 1.7. (Trends in the UK as a whole are difficult to portray accurately because of the many differences in definitions and categories which impair comparison with Scotland and Northern Ireland. By and large, however, the same tendencies can be observed in all parts of the UK.) The figure, derived from agricultural census data, shows that the number of holdings has been declining continuously since 1950, but not at

Figure 1.7. Agricultural holdings by size-groups, England and Wales (excludes holdings of less than 2 ha crops and grass).

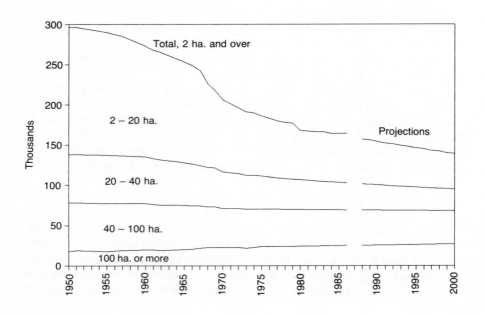

a steady rate. The decline accelerated sharply between 1965 and 1975, after which it slowed down. Indeed, between 1984 and 1986 no change in the total number was recorded.

The structural change since 1950 has largely consisted of a disappearance of 100,000 holdings of 2–20 ha, with substantial but less dramatic losses from the medium size-groups and an increase approaching 50% in the number of large farms of 100 ha or more. These now account for more than half the total land area.

There are marked differences between regions in the extent to which land is now concentrated in large farms, and in the rate at which that process is continuing. In eastern England 75% of the crops and grass area is now in holdings of 100 ha or more. In Wales and in the west and north-west of England the proportion is still generally well below 50%. During the 1980s the increase in farm size has been going ahead more rapidly in the regions where farms were already relatively large (East Anglia and the East Midlands) than in the regions where smaller farms predominate (Wales, north and north-west England and Northern Ireland). The structural differences have therefore been widening between the regions characterized by arable and pasture farming respectively.

The forces which give rise to changes in the size-structure appear to have lost much of their momentum. This is also borne out by Figure 1.8, which shows that whereas the relatively large holdings (here defined as

Figure 1.8. Percentage share of holdings of over 300 acres (121 ha) in the total crops and grass area of England and Wales.

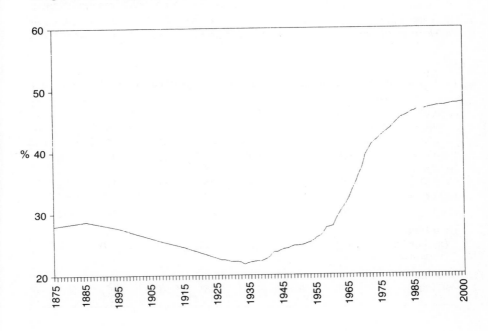

those exceeding 300 acres, because for most of the period covered by this long-term graph groupings in hectares were not available) are much more important now than they were before 1939, they are no longer increasing their share of the total area at anything like the rapid rate which prevailed between 1950 and 1970. It would seem that most of the economies of scale – which are widely acknowledged to exist but are not always clear-cut – may now have been taken up. It should also be noted that in the 1970s there were substantial financial incentives to farm size growth, in the shape of negative real costs of borrowing on mortgage, prospects of real capital gains on investment in land, taxation reliefs, and other benefits which have since been reduced.

It may be that the technical and economic pressures towards enlargement are still strong, but that the opportunities for acquisition of land are much reduced compared with 20 years ago. However, some shrinking of the 20–40 and 40–100 ha groups is still discernible, while the number of holdings of 100 ha or more continues its slow but steady expansion.

Figure 1.7 includes projections to the year 2000 which have been made on the basis of trends in the latest 10 years for which figures are available at the time of writing. They suggest that if no new influences begin to affect the size of holdings, their total number may fall by about 25,000. Most of this reduction will be the result of absorption of holdings of less than 40 ha into larger farms.

Table 1.4 gives a summary of this situation. It shows that the rate of change in the number of holdings has been inversely proportional to their size; in other words, the larger the holding, the higher have been its prospects of survival. This reflects the severe income problems experienced on very many small farms, to the extent that a land area which could support a family at a reasonably acceptable standard of living in one

Table 1.4 Number of holdings by size-group in England and Wales (000 holdings).

Area of crops and grass (ha)	1950	1960	1970	1980	1986	Projection to 2000	% change 1950–86
2–20	158	139	89	62	61	44	−61
20–40	60	58	45	37	34	27	−43
40–100	60	57	48	45	44	41	−27
100 or more	18	20	23	24	25	27	+43
Total	296	273	206	168	164	139	−45
Total area (million ha crops and grass)	10.00	9.87	9.63	9.47	9.55	(9.0)	−4.5
Average size of holding (ha)	34	36	47	56	58	(65)	+71

decade would find them struggling at the margins of survival in the next. This unhappy situation will be returned to later. Meanwhile, those who too readily deplore the disappearance of small farms should contemplate what the present income situation might be, if the total agricultural income which the market and the government can now provide to farmers and growers in England and Wales was being shared between 300,000 holdings, instead of the 160,000 indicated by the table. Alternatively they might consider by how much the price of food might have to rise if all the small farmers of the 1950s (or their successors) were still with us and were to be enabled to attain the standard of living which is now regarded as acceptable.

Size of enterprises

Just as farms have been becoming fewer and larger, so have the units of the production enterprises. These will be illustrated by reference to cereals, potatoes and milk, but the same tendencies could be found in other products and they took place more rapidly in poultry and pig enterprises.

As in the case of farm size, it is noticeable that the rate of enlargement of some enterprises, if not all, has been slowing down in recent years. Figure 1.9 shows that in the UK the number of holdings on which cereals are grown has fallen from 172,000 in 1967 to 87,000 in 1988. At the same time the average cereals area per holding growing cereals has increased

Figure 1.9. Cereal growers: number and average area in the UK (with exponential and linear projections).

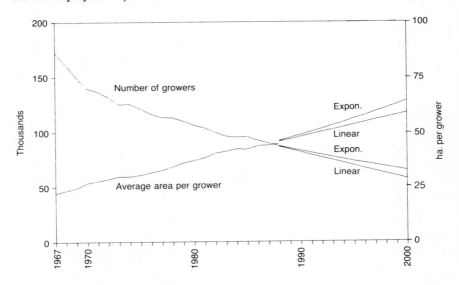

from 22 to 45 ha (right hand scale). The trend projections suggest that by the year 2000 the number of cereals producers might have fallen to about 60,000, with an average area of about 60 ha.

A very similar picture is found (Figure 1.10) with regard to potatoes, though the number of growers has fallen even more dramatically than in the case of cereals. There was very little scope for expanding potato production at the expense of the import trade, whereas in cereals about one-third of UK supplies were imported in 1967. Cereals area could therefore be expanded, under the protection of the EC's threshold prices imposed against imports from non-member countries; but potato growers were already supplying nearly all of the UK market requirements. This meant that the total area of potatoes fell steadily year by year; and if the technical factors dictated an increase in the area per grower, the number of growers had to be sharply reduced – from 105,000 in 1967 to 31,000 in 1988. The projections suggest a possible further shrinkage to 16,000 growers in the year 2000, with an average area of 8–9 ha.

The case of dairy cows (Figure 1.11) is perhaps the most interesting, and the most unpredictable, of the three enterprises chosen here by way of illustration. The number of herds in the UK fell from 132,000 in 1967 to 48,000 in 1988, while the average size of herd rose from 24 to 61 cows. There is at present much uncertainty as to whether the imposition of quotas, which has already reduced the size of the national dairy herd from 3.3 million cows in 1983 to 2.9 million in 1988, will have its main impact

Figure 1.10. Potato growers: number and average area in the UK (with exponential and linear projections).

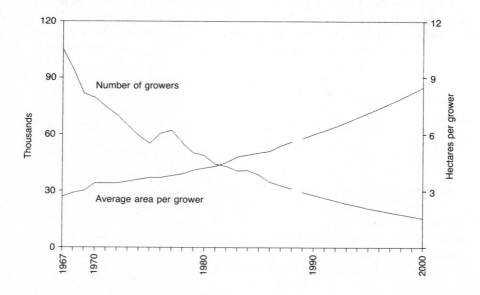

Figure 1.11. Number of dairy herds and their average size in the UK (with projections to year 2000).

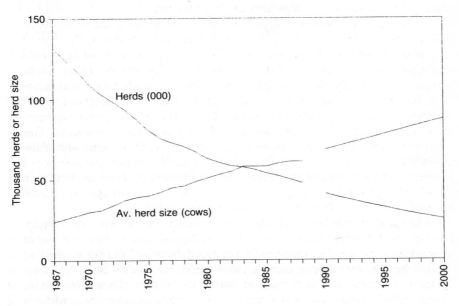

on the number of producers or on their average herd size. Figure 1.11 suggests that the steady rise in herd size, at a rate of about two cows per year which prevailed before 1983 may now have lost its momentum and even have come to an end. Yet it seems unlikely that the economic pressures on the smaller herds (of less than, say, 40 cows) have been in any way relaxed. Now that there is a market in quota (Milk Marketing Board (1989) showed that over 40% of a sample of costed dairy farms acquired quota during 1988/9), the interruption to the trend in average herd size may prove to be short-lived, and perhaps by the year 2000 we shall have only about 25,000 producers with an average herd size of 85 to 90 cows, making up a national herd of about 2.2 million (Table 1.5). However, these projections are highly conjectural. The interplay of technical, economic and social forces is highly complex, and their relative strengths could change significantly in quite a short period of time.

Employment

Of all the trends to be seen in British agriculture, the most persistent has been the decline in the labour force. Apart from a short period during and immediately after World War II, this decline has been continuing for well over a hundred years. The period of most rapid reduction in the number of

Table 1.5 Size and structure of the national dairy herd.

	Number of dairy herds (000)	Av. size of herd (cows)	Total number of dairy cows (million)
1970	110	30	3.24
1975	81	40	3.24
1980	63	51	3.23
1985	54	58	3.15
1988	48	61	2.91
	Exponential trend	Linear trend	Derived from previous columns
2000?	25	88	2.20

hired workers was in the 1960s, during which the annual rate of decline reached over 5% (Figure 1.12). This followed closely upon the time of great increase in the number of tractors on farms in the period 1945–60, and there is little doubt that mechanization was the main reason for the decline in the labour force. As has been shown, there has been no reduction in the volume of production; it has steadily expanded. The substitution of capital for labour has meant that output per person employed has risen substantially, year after year.

However, it is equally clear that the reduction in the labour force has been slowing down, in a way which resembles the loss of momentum already observed in other changes in agriculture, notably in the rate of farm enlargement. In the period from 1977 to 1988 the annual rate of decline in the total labour force (including farmers, managers, working partners and spouses) was only 1.6%. Investment in machinery, vehicles, buildings and works has also been declining, and opportunities for labour-saving on farms have evidently diminished. The long-term decline in the hired labour force has not meant that farmers' total expenditure on wages has shown a corresponding decrease. The real weekly earnings of farm workers have shown a substantial increase from the very low levels which prevailed in the immediate post-war years. In real terms, therefore, the total labour bill has remained fairly stable for a long period.

Set alongside the decline in the real net income of farmers, this means that the workers' share in the net product of agriculture has increased (Table 1.6), and the gap between their annual average earnings and the average incomes of farmers from their farming activities has narrowed. In this respect the status of the farm workers has certainly shown a marked improvement, and that status has been undergoing transformation from that of 'labourer' to that of 'technician' capable of taking vital decisions and using elaborate modern equipment.

Figure 1.12. Agricultural labour force in the UK. Workers and total (including farmers and spouses) in full-time equivalents.

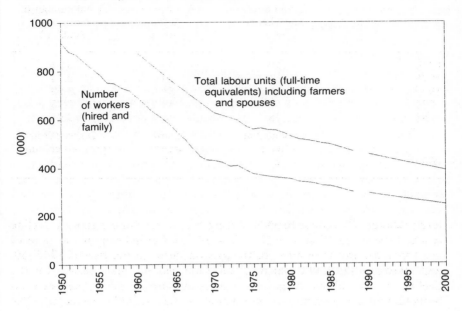

Table 1.6 The agricultural labour force and its remuneration.

| | Workers (hired and family) (000) | Total labour force[a] (full-time equiv.) (000) | Farmers and family as % of total | Real weekly earnings of farm workers (index: 1980=100) | Share in value of agric. net product[b] | |
					labour %	farming income %
1960	693	876	52	64	44	49
1965	551	745	55	71	38	52
1970	430	627	58	78	34	53
1975	375	559	59	98	40	52
1980	352	529	60	100	48	35
1985	324	497	61	111	51	27
1988	297	474	63	113	52	28

Notes: [a]Author's estimates, based on various MAFF publications.
[b]The balance was paid as rent and interest.

The work contribution of members of the farm family has not diminished as rapidly as the hired labour force, with the result that more than half the total amount of farm work is now done by farmers and their family helpers. This has been a gradual change, and it seems likely to continue. It is a far cry from the situation a century ago, when farm workers outnumbered farmers by about four to one.

By the year 2000 it seems that we might expect to have a total agricultural labour force some 15% smaller than at present, with an increasing preponderance of the family element, and probably more work being done under contract by firms carrying out specific tasks at certain times of the year. It is also to be expected that an increasing part of the total number of persons working 'on farms' will be engaged in tasks other than primary production, with the increasing emphasis on preparation of produce for the market and on diversification into gainful non-farming occupations. The 'agricultural' labour force as such will become more difficult to identify, both statistically and socially. On the changes in relative social status, see Newby (1979, 1987), and Russell (1986).

Land ownership and tenure

Present situation

Rather less than two-thirds of farmland in the UK is farmed directly by the owners and rather more than one-third by tenants.

The occupiers of farms cannot be classified simply as owners or tenants, because there is a considerable amount of mixed tenure, in which part of the farm is owned by the occupier and part is rented. Very few of the large farms (400 ha and over) are wholly rented. In England and Wales, 22% of all agricultural holdings are of mixed tenure. They are generally larger in size than wholly owner-occupied or wholly tenanted farms, so that they account for 35% of the total area. Often they are found to belong to a relatively dynamic and expanding element in farming.

Most of the land is owned by private individuals or families, but a good deal is in the hands of the Crown Commissioners, the Ecclesiastical Commissioners, the Oxford and Cambridge Colleges, local authorities, government departments and financial institutions (Table 1.7). There are no official statistics to indicate the respective shares of these categories of owners, but the following estimates were prepared by the Northfield Committee of Inquiry into the Acquisition and Occupancy of Agricultural Land in 1978 and are unlikely to have undergone any great change since that date. The financial institutions increased their land purchases for a time, but with the deterioration in the outlook for profitability in farming they have been disinvesting in recent years.

Discretionary trusts are the predominant form of ownership in the

Table 1.7 Agricultural land ownership in Great Britain, 1978.

Category of owner	Area owned	
	million hectares	%
Public and semi-public bodies and traditional institutions	1.5	8.5
Financial institutions	0.2	1.2
Private individuals, companies and trusts	16.0	90.3
All owners	17.7	100.0

Source: Northfield Report, 1979.

private sector. This is but one reflection of the imperative concern with tax-effectiveness which understandably prevails in matters relating to inheritance and succession and which must go a long way to explain the remarkable resilience of the larger landowners in the face of a distinctly hostile social climate.

The number of owners of farmland in the UK is probably in the region of 200,000, though estimates will vary according to the lower limit of area which is imposed in the enumeration. Only a small number of these – perhaps 5,000 – are estate-owners in the traditional sense of landlords each having a number of tenant-farmers from whom they receive rent.

Average farm rents are now about £100 per ha, but about one-third is taken up by landowners' costs of repairs and maintenance and other charges, so that the net rent often amounts to no more than 2% of the capital value.

In times of rapid inflation (1974–81) the real rate of interest on mortgages or other loans for land purchase was negative and therefore an incentive rather than a deterrent to those wishing to buy land; but in more recent years, with higher rates of interest and the persistence of high land prices, owner-occupiers with large loans to repay and a reduced level of farm profit have found themselves in a very difficult financial situation.

At the same time, these conditions make it almost impossible for young people without farming connections to find a means of entry. Others who have farms which are too small to provide an acceptable income find that land is not available on terms which they can begin to consider. In such a restricted land market, with very few sales except in large blocks and with hardly any new tenancies available, the 'farming ladder' leading from smaller to larger holdings has virtually disappeared. Management plans aiming at the optimum adjustment of land area to other farming resources (notably machinery and labour) to take proper account of technical changes are frustrated.

The prices realized for farms in the few sales which take place in the open market are increasingly difficult to interpret, in that they usually relate to a house and other buildings as well as to land. Many prospective buyers, especially in the south and south Midlands of England, are showing at least as much interest in the residential and amenity values of the properties as in the prospects for profitable farming from the land itself. To express price in £ per ha or per acre is of no great help to a true appreciation of the farmland market when a substantial part of the price is attributable to the residence and the style of living which it offers. For the same reason, attempts to estimate the current or prospective 'agricultural' return on capital are problematical.

Farmland prices vary greatly from region to region, and are usually higher per hectare on the smaller farms – again showing the influence of house values on the total price. Recently average prices in England for farms with vacant possession have been of the order of £3,500 per ha, which in real terms is well below the abnormal peaks reached in 1972–3 and 1978–80, and is not much higher than the level prevailing in the 1960s. Rather surprisingly in view of the farm income situation, the downward trend in real land prices after 1979 appears to have been halted in 1987.

In Wales prices are generally lower than in England, and lower still in Scotland where rough grazing land is so extensive.

Trends

In the past hundred years there has been a substantial decline in the prevalence of the landlord–tenant system and a marked increase in owner-occupation. This change has been so far-reaching as to be described as representing 'the disintegration of the traditional rural class structure' (Newby et al., 1978).

The status of landowners relative both to farmers and to farmworkers has certainly diminished, and their share in the value of the product of agriculture has been sharply eroded since the so-called Golden Age of farming in 1850–75. At that time about 20% of the net product accrued to landowners as net rent (i.e. after allowing for landlords' expenses for repairs and maintenance); at the present time the proportion is only 3%. Most of this shift of economic and social importance away from the landowners took place between 1921 and 1939, partly as the result of new laws which gave greater security to tenants, but also reflecting the more stringent taxation of hereditary wealth and 'unearned income'.

Numerically, most of the owners of agricultural land in the UK today are farmers whose mode of living is shaped by profits, not rents. The 'tenantry' is a much reduced group, while many of the remaining landed gentry have become much more closely identified with farming. In many cases they have extended the part of the estate which they farm themselves, by taking land in hand when suitable tenancies fall vacant. This not only enabled them to reduce their 'unearned' income, which for a long period was taxed at higher rates than were applied to farming profits, but also opened the way to the economies of scale which were already being turned to account by the larger owner-occupiers and mixed-tenure farmers.

The trend towards owner-occupation is shown in Table 1.8 and Figure 1.13. These show two main features: a rapid transfer from the landlord–tenant system to owner-occupation between 1919 and 1960; and a much

Table 1.8 Land tenure, GB: percentage of farmland rented.

1887	85	1976	44
1908	88	1982	41
1914	89	1984	40
1922	82	1985	39
1950	62	1986	39
1960	51	1987	38
1970	45		

Sources: MAFF (1968) and MAFF *Agricultural Statistics* (various dates).
The figures relate to the total area of holdings which were wholly or mainly tenanted. In N. Ireland nearly all land is owner-occupied.

Figure 1.13. Land tenure in Great Britain: percentage of farmland rented.

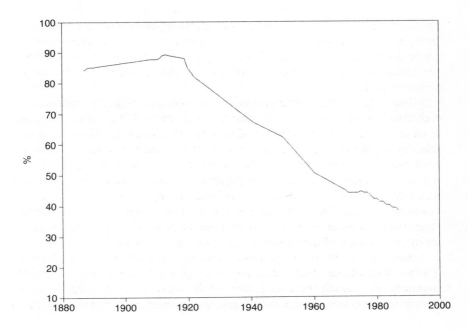

slower movement since 1960, but in the same direction. The figures should be taken as being indicative rather than precise. They probably somewhat overstate the amount of rented land, because family partnership arrangements result in land being returned as rented by the occupier from the partnership when the real situation is for all practical purposes that of owner-occupation. For this reason the rented proportion is probably closer to one-third, as indicated at the beginning of this section.

Prospects

The future pattern of land tenure seems likely to be influenced as much by political as by economic factors. The small, but still powerful, part of the population which owns land feels itself threatened by the questioning and often openly hostile attitude of those who challenge the assumption that the legal ownership of land carries with it the rights of exclusive use. The slogan: 'This land is our land' is voiced on both sides of this social division. Private landowners may be constrained, by planning controls or by economic incentives authorized by the government, to revise the concept of ownership to accommodate some of the 'rights' now being asserted by others.

So long as the electorate continues to give power to Conservative governments, the egalitarian pressures which have been exerted from time to time throughout this century can hardly be expected to bring about the abolition or even the drastic erosion of family inheritance, either of land or of other assets. Nevertheless the owners of land have become noticeably more defensive about the extent and justification of their personal and family wealth, and about their ability to preserve it for succeeding generations. Planning and investment horizons have been perceptibly shortened.

Meanwhile others, here and abroad, who have money but are not yet landowners in this country are showing confidence in land as an investment. In spite of the fall in farming profitability which has been experienced in the 1980s, there has been no corresponding collapse in the farmland market. Neither inheritance taxes nor the statements of intention about a wealth tax appear to have shaken the belief that land is a secure asset, although it must be said that the farmland market has not been very active, and prices have been registered on a very narrow base of transactions.

In face of the evidence that the traditional landlord–tenant system has been steadily retreating in favour of owner-occupation, there are still many people whose experience of the system has convinced them of its effectiveness and its vitality. Given mutually satisfactory provisions relating to security of tenure on the one hand and the right to make reasonable adjustments to rents on the other, the system has much to commend it, combining as it does two very different sets of capacities. There appears to be no shortage of willing tenants who are well qualified for farming but cannot command the vast amount of capital needed to buy their way in as owner-occupiers, or cannot undertake the burdensome repayment terms which ownership would entail.

The survival of tenancy in one form or another seems to be highly likely; what may change is the pattern of ownership, as between traditional family landed estates, financial institutions and public authorities (see Table 1.7). In the Northfield Report (1979), the Committee stated that

> on agricultural grounds we see no reason to wish to hasten the departure of the good private landlord . . . but most of us believe that it is unrealistic to suppose that the private landlord's stake in agriculture can remain at its present size without considerable assistance.

The Committee expected that ownership by financial institutions would increase, depending on the rate at which private owners of let land found themselves obliged to sell their estates, but not beyond an upper limit of 11% of the agricultural area of Great Britain by the year 2020; and the share held by public and semi-public bodies and traditional institutions was expected to remain stable at 8–9%.

References

Burrell, A., Hill, B. and Medland, J. (1987) *Statistical Handbook of UK Agriculture*, 3rd edn. Department of Agricultural Economics, Wye College, University of London.

MAFF (Ministry of Agriculture, Fisheries and Food) (1968) *A Century of Agricultural Statistics, Great Britain 1866–1966*.

Marks, H.F. and Britton, D.K. (eds) (1989) *A Hundred Years of British Food and Farming: A Statistical Survey*. Taylor & Francis, London.

Milk Marketing Board (1989) *An Analysis Of Farm Management Services Costed Dairy Farms, 1988–89*. FMS Information Unit Report No.67.

Murphy, M.C. (1985) *Report on Farming in the Eastern Counties of England, 1983–84*. Department of Land Economy, University of Cambridge.

Newby, H. (1979) *Green and Pleasant Land?* Hutchinson, Reading.

Newby, H. (1987) *Country Life*. Weidenfeld & Nicholson, London.

Newby, H., Bell, C., Rose, D. and Saunders, P. (1978) *Property, Paternalism and Power: Class and Control in Rural England*. Hutchinson, Reading.

Northfield Report (1979) Report of the Committee of Inquiry into the Acquisition and Occupancy of Agricultural Land. Cmnd.7599. HMSO, London.

Peters, G.H. (1988) Agriculture. In: *Reviews of United Kingdom Statistical Sources*, Vol.XXIII. Chapman and Hall, for Royal Statistical Society and Economic and Social Research Council, London.

Russell, A. (1986) *The Country Parish*. SPCK, London.

Appendix on statistics of numbers of holdings

There are no official statistics dealing with numbers or sizes of 'farms' (Peters, 1988). The unit employed for census purposes is the 'holding', a term which may be applied to any piece of land which is being used for agricultural purposes. It is customary to prescribe a 'threshold' or minimum size below which a census return is not required. This minimum may be expressed in terms of area, employment or output, or some combination of these. In recent years MAFF has differentiated between 'main' and 'minor' holdings and in some of its statistics minor holdings are excluded.

More troublesome from the point of view of the study of structural trends is the fact that from time to time MAFF has changed its definitions relating to census enumeration. For example, in June 1968 about 47,000 holdings which had previously been enumerated were excluded because their agricultural output was considered to be negligible, individually and even in total. Other exclusions followed at intervals. This makes it difficult to draw any conclusions about structural change from a straightforward consideration of the changing numbers of holdings as shown in the published statistics.

Most of the holdings affected by these successive exclusions were of less than 2 ha (5 acres) of crops and grass. By confining attention through-out the whole period to holdings of 2 ha or more we have been able to avoid the major artificial breaks in the time-series, which would otherwise be very apparent. One result of this tidying-up is that a certain number of glasshouse units and intensive pig or poultry units will have been excluded. This would be an important omission if changes in the structure of produc-tion or of incomes were being considered but for present purposes broad changes in the land-use structure are being looked at, and in this context more is gained than lost by applying the 2 ha minimum.

There remains, however, another change in statistical practice which has given rise to some divergence between the apparent trends shown in the published figures and the real trends which they partly conceal. From about 1970 onwards, efforts have been made to prevent separate returns being registered for holdings which are farmed with one or more other holdings as part of a single farm unit. This 'statistical amalgamation' will have somewhat overstated the real tendency towards farm amalgamation which has been going on throughout the period under review. The effect is unlikely to have been very significant, but it is known that some 10,000 holdings were so treated between 1969 and 1970. This word of caution therefore seems justified.

One further pitfall in this field relates to the use of figures of the 'average size' of holdings, notably when making international comparisons. Average size is calculated by dividing a figure for total area by a figure for total number of holdings. It will be evident that such a calculation will be highly sensitive to any changes through time, or any differences between countries, in the 'threshold size' limit which is applied for census purposes. The sudden elimination of tens of thousands of very small holdings will have no perceptible effect on the total area recorded, but a dramatic upward effect on the average.

The figure for average size will also be greatly influenced by the decision whether or not to include rough grazing land in the farm area. This inclusion is the usual practice in European Community statistics. Largely because of the vast areas of rough grazing in Scotland, the practice has the effect of raising the average size of UK holdings by over 50% above the size as measured in terms of crops and grass area.

These are other reasons why, for the purpose of the present study of trends, the procedure of excluding all holdings of less than 2 ha throughout the period has been adopted, and observations have been confined to crops and grass area – a decision which, incidentally, results at the present time in the exclusion of some 8,000 holdings in England and Wales consisting entirely of rough grazings.

Chapter 2
The Changing Place of Farming

Ian Hodge

Farming for the nation

Since the Second World War, agriculture has experienced a period of sustained government intervention; initially under the aegis of the 1947 Agriculture Act and, since entry into the European Economic Community (EEC), under the Common Agricultural Policy (CAP). In this respect, agriculture has received special treatment, quite different from that accorded to other industries. This treatment reflects a special view of agriculture, which has, over much of the period, enjoyed common assent.

During the Second World War, agriculture was called upon to play a special role in the defence of a beleaguered nation. By all accounts, it was not found wanting. Government took close rein over the operations of food production, but control at a local level was undertaken by the farmers themselves through the County War Agricultural Executive Committees. Incentives were provided for a wide range of improvements, such as subsidies for ploughing up permanent pasture, underdrainage, liming and land reclamation. While called upon to make unusual efforts and sacrifices, the levels of guaranteed prices enabled farmers to increase their prosperity. Self and Storing (1962) comment that, by the end of the war, farmers had a considerable preference for a full system of guaranteed prices, even with its concomitant of state control.

Subsequently, the position of agriculture was much influenced by the events during the war. There was a general appreciation of the farmers' achievements, and an ensuing pressure for the expansion of food production in a period of food shortages and strategic concerns. Among agricultural organizations there was a unanimous desire for a system of state control and guaranteed prices to achieve this. This consensus over the appropriate direction for agricultural policy was also shared by the major political parties. The 1947 Agriculture Act, enacted by the incoming Labour Government, followed closely the outlines of a legislative measure which had been drawn up by the previous government (Self and Storing, 1962).

The arguments for agricultural support also went beyond the narrow concern for food production. The Scott Committee, reporting in 1942, believed that the maintenance of agriculture would have the effect of reviving the country life and of bringing about an improvement in the physical and social standards of country areas. Further, a prosperous agriculture was seen as the only way of preserving the countryside in anything like its traditional aspect. The countryside, it was argued, must be farmed if it is to retain those features which give it distinctive charm and character. At that time, the threat to the quality of the agricultural landscape was perceived as arising from neglect and disuse; a view based on the experience of agricultural depression in the 1930s when areas of farm land were derelict and abandoned. Dennison, in his Minority report to the Scott Report, was critical of the majority views. He anticipated that agricultural development would be associated with declining employment and queried whether the preservation of the rural environment was best done by supporting traditional agriculture. Similarly, Hall (1948) perceived that some of the characteristic features of the countryside which the Scott Committee attributed to the needs of agriculture, such as hedgerows and small woodlands, could in practice be a nuisance to farming. However, he believed that their removal could improve the visual aspect of the landscape which he regarded as 'overcrowded and fidgety'. But the clear majority view saw a prosperous agriculture as being an essential requirement of a prosperous rural economy and an attractive countryside. And this represented the views held more widely.

The framework established for the control of agriculture in the 1947 Act was retained without fundamental change up to the 1970s. During this time, notwithstanding fluctuations in farm incomes and disagreements over the administration of policy, a close, perhaps symbiotic, relationship was retained between the Ministry of Agriculture, Fisheries and Food (MAFF) and the agricultural industry, as particularly represented by the National Farmers' Union (NFU). The validity of supporting agriculture and the objective of boosting domestic food production were held largely without question. The National Farmers' Union played a direct role in the determination of policy, especially with regard to the annual price review. The 1947 Act required the government to consult representatives of the industry, which was interpreted to mean the NFU. Over this period, it maintained a reputation for being a strong, efficient and influential pressure group acting on behalf of farmers. Indeed, it has been regarded as one of the most effective pressure groups in Britain (Grant, 1983).

During this post-war period, there was a considerable measure of agreement between the major political parties regarding support for agriculture. The deficiency payments support system enabled farmers to be supported and food to be traded on the United Kingdom market at world prices, thus justifying the claim of providing cheap food for consumers. The cost of this was the burden on taxpayers.

Farming in the European Community

The debate over entry into the EEC in the early 1970s brought the discussion about agriculture, the area of policy most developed within the EEC to the fore. The objectives of the CAP, enshrined in the Treaty of Rome in 1957, were couched in similar terms to those of the 1947 Agriculture Act. However, the mechanism used to support farm incomes differed, in that it generally held domestic food prices above world prices so that the greatest burden of support was switched from the taxpayer to the consumer. In fact, the British system of support had been changed in this direction prior to entry to the EEC, but the effect of entry on food prices was a major concern.

Adoption of the CAP in many respects sowed the seeds for the more recent criticism of agricultural policy and, partly because they have been perceived as having done well from it, the criticism has been transferred to farmers themselves. The debate over entry was prolonged by the initial rebuff, the subsequent successful negotiations and then by the renegotiation and referendum. Even once the debate about entry was essentially concluded, criticisms of the CAP from this side of the Channel persisted, prompted by the particularly disadvantageous position of the UK. Rising food costs at this time were largely attributed to the EEC (Documentary Research, 1973). Further, as the UK was a significant net importer of agricultural products, the CAP tended to transfer funds from UK consumers to farmers in other EEC countries. Similarly, and perhaps causing even more vexation, the contributions made by the UK to the EEC development budget were popularly conceived as going to inefficient 'French peasants'. These persistent concerns have kept up the public awareness of the problems of agricultural policy, as the press has reported with varying degrees of scepticism the regular shuttling of politicians to and from Brussels in an attempt to restrain total agricultural spending, or else get some of our money back.

However, British concern at the finances of the CAP did not lead to a policy of restricting domestic production. On the contrary, the official position was to encourage the further expansion of farm output. The government view was set out in two White Papers during the 1970s. In 1975, *Food From Our Own Resources* (MAFF) stated that 'The Government take the view that a continuing expansion of food production in Britain will be in the national interest'. *Farming and the Nation* (MAFF, 1979) was a little more cautious, but still reached a similar conclusion. This was despite the recognition in the same document that within the European Community, the problem for several commodities was one of surplus rather than shortage.

One explanation for this lies in a fundamental weakness of the CAP. The principle of common financing means that the costs of supporting any increased British production, which subsequently goes into intervention, are shared between all of the member countries. This incentive, of course, applies to any individual country taking a national view of its financial position. Thus, while production restraint is in the interests of the Community taken as a whole, it is not necessarily in the interests of the individual member countries. And this, of course, adds to the complexity of attempts to restrain EEC expenditure on the CAP.

The rôle of the NFU has been changed by UK entry into the EEC. The ending of the formal position which it enjoyed under the 1947 Act and the need for agricultural policy to be agreed between all the member countries, have inevitably reduced its ability to influence policy directly, although perhaps to a lesser extent than might have been anticipated (Grant, 1983). The NFU has continued to exert its influence over MAFF decisions, which, given a significant direct UK government expenditure on agriculture and the opportunity for UK governments to influence prices via the green exchange rates, continue to have an important impact on agricultural prosperity.

The end of consensus?

In the immediate post-war period there seems to have been a strong consensus in support of agriculture both with regard to its rôle in food production and in respect of its wider contribution to rural communities and the countryside. More recently, this widespread support has come under attack from a number of directions (see e.g. Peters, 1986). The two central elements of this attack have concerned the costs of the CAP and of the consequences of agricultural change for the environment. Together they have threatened the image and the position of the agricultural sector to an extent which has not been experienced over the past 40 years.

The first line of attack has not been aimed directly at farmers themselves, but rather at the agricultural policy which supports them. Indeed, a major protagonist in the debate, Richard Body, is a farmer himself. The main criticisms of the policy had been made much earlier by academics, but their careful style failed to create much impact. It took an apparently permanent 'crisis' in European finances and polemics, particularly Body's (1982) *The Triumph and the Shame*, to put the question on the centre stage of public debate.

The second line of attack has been directed towards the activities undertaken by farmers themselves and the consequences which these have had on the rural environment. Early criticisms in the UK were associated with the growth of environmental awareness in the early 1970s and tended to be associated with the loss of specific features, especially hedgerows. In 1974, the Countryside Commission published *New Agricultural Landscapes* which documented the changes taking place. The Nature Conservancy Council also detailed impacts in *Nature Conservation and*

Agriculture, in 1977. However, in this case too, a more polemical book by Marion Shoard (1980), *The Theft of the Countryside* had the effect of putting the issue firmly into the public arena. The debate preceding the 1981 Wildlife and Countryside Act then further raised the level of public consciousness and provided the stimulus for conservationists to co-ordinate their actions in support of the rural environment. Cox and Lowe (1983) have described the politics of the Act. The debate about the Act, in the context of other pressures on agriculture, led to a wider discussion throughout the media about the relationship between modern agriculture and the environment and the responsibilities of farmers. The passage of the legislation provided a forum for a trial of strength between the agricultural and environmental interests. This competition for influence has been examined by Cox *et al.* (1986).

Beyond these two major assaults on the position of agriculture, other issues have been simmering, and occasionally boiling over to become the centre of attention. The health lobby has mounted strong criticisms of some of the basic products of British agriculture. Milk, especially, for years regarded as the cornerstone of a healthy diet for children, is now under suspicion for its high cholesterol content.

Perhaps more damaging to the image of the industry has been a series of health scares which have rocked various sectors, especially, salmonella in poultry and egg production, listeria in cheese and patés, BSE (bovine spongiform encephalopathy) in beef production and the use of alar on apples. These have caused widespread questioning of the production methods used and in some instances substantial rejection of the products produced. Similarly, animal rights campaigners have attacked the conditions under which many farm animals are kept, especially those in intensive livestock units. These movements together have had an important impact on the patterns of food consumption and the attitudes of consumers towards agriculture.

These influences have had their impacts on the nature and administration of agricultural policy. A landmark in the process of policy adjustment was reached with the introduction of milk quotas in April 1984. This represented an important break in policy-making following a longer period over which the budgetary pressures for change had been building up. The political processes from which milk quotas arose have been analysed in detail by Petit *et al.* (1987).

The first sign of change within the MAFF, in response to environmental concerns came in 1984 with the establishment of an Environmental Co-ordination Unit. In 1986, the remit of the Ministry was widened by the Agriculture Act so as to have regard to, and to endeavour to achieve a reasonable balance between, the following considerations:

1. The promotion and maintenance of a stable and efficient agricultural industry;

2. The economic and social interest of rural areas;

3. The conservation and enhancement of the natural beauty and amenity of the countryside (including its flora and fauna and geological and physiographical features) and of any features of archeological interest there; and

4. the promotion of the enjoyment of the countryside by the public.

By 1987, the government's view about the value of food production had been reversed. In February of that year, the Minister, Michael Jopling, said that the European Community was now producing surpluses in many of the main agricultural commodities; it no longer made sense to simply maintain and expand UK food production. It is notable that the problem of surplus production had been officially identified in 1979, but that at that time this had not led to a policy of restraint. In his 1987 statement the Minister continued that

> a new balance of policies has to be struck, with less support for expanding production; more attention to the demands of the market; more encouragement for alternative uses of the land; more response to the claims of the environment; and more diversity on farms and in the rural economy.

However, the changes so far have not silenced many of the critics of the way in which agriculture is administered. Many argue that the relationship between the industry and MAFF continues to be too close to be healthy. Various reorganizations of ministerial responsibilities have been proposed, especially that responsibility for food quality should be within a Ministry of Health rather than Agriculture and the Department of the Environment should have wider remit over issues affecting the countryside. Some have proposed a new Ministry of Rural Affairs.

The position of the NFU has also shifted, recognizing the changing times and seeking to lead in the evolution of new policies. The 1984 policy statement *The Way Forward* recognized the need for a reappraisal of expansionist policies and the public concern for the environmental impact of agriculture. New integrated policies should be developed to cover the whole complex of farming, rural development and environmental needs. The NFU proposed policies to encourage alternative land uses and accepted the need for some environmental controls.

The prevailing attitudes and assumptions of those involved in the policy process have come a long way since the War. The aims of agriculture have shifted from a position where increasing production was both the key objective and the means by which most other objectives would be attainable. Currently, much of the debate revolves around the limitation of production, both to ease the budgetry cost and to mitigate the environmental impact. While in general terms the type of redirection required of farming holds quite wide assent, the specifics do not. Conflict has been sharpened and a minority at various extremes campaign for a fundamentally different role for the agricultural industry. The media have given increasing prominence to the issues and to the protesting voices. On the BBC, long-established farming programmes have had to give way to countryside programmes with a very different slant and audience.

Attitudes to farming and the countryside

What changes have there been in the popular perception of agriculture and the countryside? One indication of this can be gained from opinion polls. Of course, the answers people give are subject to all sorts of influences and biases, so that the figures should be treated with some caution. A survey conducted for the National Farmers' Union in 1973 (Documentary Research Limited, 1973) found strong and positive opinions about farmers and farming. Some results of this survey are given in Table 2.1. Respondents showed a high personal regard for farmers. Farmers were thought to be efficient and the vast majority believed that the UK should produce more of its food. Only 2% of respondents thought that farmers were paid too much and only 4% that farmers were helped by government too much. The only concerns about agriculture appeared to be a dominant view that too many chemicals were used and a minority showing some anxiety about intensive production methods. At the same time, concern was expressed about urban development on agricultural land.

The high esteem for agriculture has been eroded over the years since these findings were published. This shift reflects a growing concern about

Table 2.1 Attitudes to farming 1973.

Percentages of respondents believing that:	%[a]		%[a]
1. UK should produce more of its food	84	less	1
2, Farmers are efficient	77	not	12
3. Farmers paid too little	48	too much	2
4. Farmers should be helped more by Government	49	less	4
5. Intensive production of eggs and poultry is a good thing	59	bad	32
6. Farmers help to preserve the countryside	73	do not	15
7. Amount of chemicals used in farming too much	61	too little	1
8. We are losing too much farm land to motorways	61	we are not	31
9. We are losing too much farm land to urban development	53	we are not	36
10. Percentage having high personal regard for farmers	78	low	5

Source: Documentary Research Limited (1973).
[a]Percentages do not sum to 100 due to intermediate responses and don't knows.

many of the changes which are taking place in the countryside and about the aims of agricultural policy. But at the same time the support for farmers themselves has held up. For some years, Social and Community Planning Research have included questions concerning the countryside in their annual survey of British Social Attitudes (Young, 1986, 1987, 1988). Respondents were asked to indicate the extent to which they believed that the countryside had changed in the past 20 years. In both 1986 and 1987, about half thought that it had changed a lot; this rose to 55% in 1987. About 20% thought that it was about the same. The majority of those recognizing change thought that the changes were for the worse. This represented 56% of all respondents in 1987. However, the proportion indicating that they were 'very concerned' about the changes rose from 31 to 44% over the three years.

Questions were also asked about the farmer's rôle in the countryside. Specifically, respondents were asked to indicate how much they agreed or disagreed with each of four statements:

1. Modern farming methods have caused damage to the countryside.
2. If farmers have to choose between producing more food and looking after the countryside, they should produce more food.
3. All things considered, farmers do a good job in looking after the countryside.
4. Government should withhold some subsidies from farmers and use them to protect the countryside, even if this leads to higher prices.

The results are shown in Table 2.2. While there is a belief that modern farming damages the countryside, the view that farmers do a good job of looking after the countryside continues to be very strongly held, as it was in the NFU survey in 1973. This apparent paradox was also found in a Country Landowners Association survey conducted in 1983 (Worth, 1984). Since the 1973 survey, there has been a dramatic fall in the numbers believing that food production should be expanded, although the rider relating to looking after the countryside may have influenced responses. However, it is consistent with the government view. It is also worth noting the increased level of self-sufficiency in temperate food production which

Table 2.2 The farmer's role in the countryside.

Percentages of respondents agreeing that:	1985	1987
1. Modern farming damages the countryside	63	68
2. Farmers should produce more food	53	35
3. Farmers look after the countryside well	75	74
4. Government should withhold subsidies	47	51

Source: Young (1988).

rose from 67% in 1973 to 78% in 1986. Views on subsidies also appear to have changed, although the questions cannot be directly compared.

Again, in the 1987 survey, respondents were asked to consider each of five policies:

1. Increasing the amounts of countryside being farmed.
2. Building new housing in country areas.
3. Putting the needs of farmers before protection of wildlife.
4. Providing more roads in country areas.
5. Increasing the number of picnic areas and camping sites in the country-side.

The results are detailed in Table 2.3. The strongest preference is for more picnic areas and camping sites. Over 70% of respondents opposed putting the needs of farmers before the protection of wildlife. The view against urban development, indicated in the earlier survey is continued here. These views are very similar to those in the 1986 survey.

Another opinion poll, undertaken for Compassion in World Farming in 1987, also indicates a widespread concern over the methods used in livestock production. Irrespective of religious beliefs 92% of respondents believed that animals should be humanely stunned before slaughter. Of those surveyed, 84% objected to the live export of animals for slaughter in foreign abattoirs. A total of 86% indicated that close confinement of sows should be made illegal. Finally, 67% of respondents believed that battery egg production should be banned. While the questions were somewhat different, these results appear to contrast markedly with the position in 1973 where a substantial majority favoured intensive production of pigs and poultry.

In summary, the public have held and continue to hold a high regard for farmers; there is further evidence of this in the surveys reported by Worth (1984). There is also a belief that farmers look after the countryside

Table 2.3 Attitudes to policies[a].

	Should be encouraged %	Don't mind %	Should be discouraged %	Should be stopped %
1. Increasing farmed countryside	9	31	46	9
2. Building new housing	11	22	49	15
3. Putting farmers before wildlife	8	16	57	15
4. More roads in country areas	13	27	46	10
5. More picnic and camping sites	49	28	16	4

Source: Young (1988).
[a]Based on survey conducted in 1987.

well. However, there are strong indications of concern over the changes which are taking place in the quality of the countryside and for the influence of modern farming on these. There is also a preference for the encouragement of more recreational facilities and wildlife conservation, and less regard for the demands of food production. A negative view of urban development in rural areas has persisted. Also the public appears to be much more critical of some animal welfare aspects of livestock production than it was only 15 years ago.

The changes which have taken place leave agriculture in a somewhat uncertain position within the British consciousness. After the War, agriculture played a central role in the national effort for reconstruction, easing food shortages, enhancing the strategic position of the country and protecting the countryside. Policies for agricultural support followed logically from these contributions, but times have changed and many persistent elements of an earlier agricultural policy have become an anachronism. Realignment is inevitable, but the extent and exact direction of this has yet to be determined.

References

Body, R. (1982) *Agriculture: The Triumph and the Shame.* Maurice Temple Smith, London.

Cox, G. and Lowe, P. (1983) A battle not the war; the politics of the Wildlife and Countryside Act. In: A.W. Girling (ed.) *Countryside Planning Yearbook*, 4. Geo-Books, Norwich, pp. 48–76.

Cox, G., Lowe, P. and Winter, M. (1986) Agriculture and conservation in Britain: a policy community under siege. In: Cox, G., Lowe, P. and Winter, M. (eds), *Agriculture: People and Policies.* Allen & Unwin, London, pp. 181–215.

Documentary Research Ltd (1973) A Survey of Current Attitudes of People Living in Cities and Towns Towards Farms and Farming. Documentary Research Ltd, Bristol.

Grant, W. (1983) The National Farmers' Union; the classic case of incorporation, In: Marsh, D. (ed.), *Pressure Politics: Interest Groups in Britain.* Junction Books, London, pp. 129–43.

Hall, A.D. (1941) *Reconstruction and the Land.* Macmillan, London.

MAFF (1975) *Food from Our Own Resources.* Cmnd 6020, HMSO, London.

MAFF (1979) *Farming and the Nation.* Cmnd 7458, HMSO, London.

Nature Conservancy Council (1977) *Nature Conservation and Agriculture.* Nature Conservancy Council, London.

Peters, G. (1986) British agriculture under attack. In: Cox, G., Lowe, P. and Winter, M. (eds) *Agriculture: People and Policies.* Allen & Unwin, London, pp. 160–80.

Petit, M., De Benedictis, M., Britton, D., De Groot, M., Henrichsmeyer, W. and Lechi, F. (1987) *Agricultural Policy Formation in the European Community: The Birth of Milk Quotas and CAP Reform.* Developments in Agricultural Economics, 4. Elsevier, Amsterdam.

Scott Committee (1942) *Report of the Royal Commission on Land Utilisation in Rural Areas.* Cmnd 6378. HMSO, London.

Self, P. and Storing, H.J. (1962) *The State and the Farmer.* George Allen & Unwin, London.

Shoard, M. (1980) *The Theft of the Countryside.* Temple Smith, London.

Worth, J. (1984) What we think of the countryside. *Ecos,* 5, 35–7.

Young, K. (1986) A green and pleasant land? In: Jowell, R., Witherspoon, S. and Brook, L. (eds), *British Social Attitudes: the 1986 Report.* Gower, Aldershot, pp. 59–88.

Young, K. (1987) Interim Report: The Countryside. In: Jowell, R., Witherspoon, S. and Brook, L. (eds), *British Social Attitudes: the 1987 Report.* Gower, Aldershot, pp. 153–69.

Young, K. (1988) Interim Report: Rural prospects. In: Jowell, R., Witherspoon, S. and Brook, L. (eds), *British Social Attitudes: the 5th Report.* Gower, Aldershot, pp. 155–74.

Chapter 3
Technology

John North

Introduction

Technological change has been a major feature of UK farming over many centuries; but over the last 30 years or so the rate of change has been especially significant, resulting in rapid and sustained increases in food production from a reduced land base. Farmers have shown their willingness and ability to take up and apply the new technology, increasing the efficiency in the use of resources available on the farm. Higher-yielding varieties of crop plants and the availability of better-performing animals have required larger inputs of fertilizer, feedingstuffs and pesticides to realize their potential. Farmers' purchases of goods and services for productive purposes have increased to levels quite unknown and unforeseen before 1950.

These changes often entailed some increase in borrowings, but until recent years the financial returns have generally been more than sufficient to accommodate this. It is not only in the past decade that increased expenditure by farmers has been associated with a significant rise in their bank overdrafts and other debts, both in absolute terms and as a proportion of the value of their assets.

During the period since World War II agricultural and economic policies have provided reasonable security of prices, guaranteed markets for many products and a wide range of beneficial measures aimed at the modernization of farming. This support has further stimulated the take-up of new technology. However, increases in supply with no corresponding increases in demand have led to a reduction in real prices, while at the same time there have been increases in the real costs of some inputs.

Early adopters of a successful new technology obtain the maximum benefits from the higher returns which accrue before a general increase in supply forces price levels to adjust. Other farmers are then obliged to apply the same new technology in an attempt to reduce some of their disadvantage and to make it possible to stay in business. This so-called technological treadmill will continue to operate and will be inescapable so long as innovation continues, unless governments decide to give sustained support to farm incomes to compensate for any downward pressure on market prices. The need for the less enterprising farmers to adopt new technology would then be inversely proportional to the extent of the income support afforded to them. Meanwhile the early adopters of each successive innovation would continue to profit by their action.

Prospects for improvements in plant growth

Plant growth is the basis of all agricultural production, of animals as well as of crops – though it has to be remembered that not all of the livestock on UK farms obtain all their food from plant growth originating in the UK; in 1987 the total cost of imported feed amounted to almost £600 million. Indeed, the future pattern of British farming could conceivably be considerably affected by upward or downward shifts in the degree of dependence on imported feedingstuffs. Even so, the fact remains that it is essentially the production of more crops and more grass from our fields and hill grazings which has provided the means of raising total agricultural output.

The genetic potential of a plant variety sets the limits within which environmental factors and management practices can influence plant growth. The physiological processes within the plant are the mechanisms through which genetic potentials are realized in the form of yields which have an economic value.

Developments in biotechnology have opened up new opportunities to increase their genetic potentials and to reduce losses. In typical farming conditions the production potential may, of course, be reduced by the use of suboptimal levels of inputs and by other weaknesses in management practices, especially inadequate control of diseases, pests and weeds.

The most important physiological process involved in plant growth is photosynthesis. This is the process by which green plants convert energy from the sun as radiation into chemical energy which can be stored in the plant, initially in the form of carbohydrate.

C3 and C4 plants

When the first product of photosynthesis is a three-carbon compound, the plant is called a C3 plant. All cultivated plants in the UK are C3 plants, with the exception of maize. Maize, sugar cane and tropical grasses all produce a four-carbon compound as the first product of photosynthesis, and are known as C4 plants.

Generally, C4 plants are 30–50% more efficient photosynthetically than C3 plants, in converting the sun's energy into useful dry matter. More importantly, growth rates are higher for C4 plants. When averaged over an entire growing season, maximum daily growth rates of 13 g of dry matter per m^2 per day were recorded for C3 plants, compared with 22 g for C4 cereal plant stands, although currently most C4 plants yield less than C3 plants in temperate climates. The level for the C3 cereal plants represents a conversion of the incident energy from the sun of only 2%, whereas between 6 and 9% might eventually be achieved by plants with improved photosynthetic efficiencies.

The supply of carbon dioxide to plants is also a yield-limiting factor. Increasing the amounts of carbon dioxide in the atmosphere, and also within plants, increases growth. C4 plants have the ability to utilize more of the carbon dioxide from the surrounding air. The concentration point at which the rate of carbon dioxide used for photosynthesis equals the rate of loss through respiration is 50–100 ppm for C3 plants, but C4 plants can reduce the concentration level to 0–10 ppm. This is important in field crops, where raising carbon dioxide levels within and above the crop by supplementation is impracticable.

Respiration is the process which provides the plant with energy for growth from the products of photosynthesis. However, respiration levels above the needs of the crop for growth, maintenance and production are wasteful. Regulation of respiration is therefore important in crop production. Respiration takes place to some extent in the light, but more particularly in the dark. In C3 plants the loss of dry matter from respiration increases between two and four times for each 10°C temperature rise in the range 0–35°C. At temperatures above 25°C many C3 plants are unproductive. In contrast, losses from C4 plants are largely unaffected by temperature change within this range.

In C3 plants a second type of respiration, stimulated only by light and known as photorespiration, contributes to the loss of plant dry matter. As this does not occur in C4 plants it is probably not an essential function and its reduction or elimination could produce yield increases.

The efficiency in the use of water and plant nutrients is also higher in C4 plants. In England (Austin, 1980) it has been estimated that lack of water reduces cereal yields by 10–20%. The highest yield losses occur in the lower rainfall areas, where cereal growing tends to be concentrated. Water shortage reduces yields in many other crops.

All these considerations suggest that there would be a productivity advantage if the desirable characteristics of C4 plants could be transferred into the C3 crops grown in the UK. This might be done either by transforming C3 plants into modified C4 plants, or by transferring one or more of the beneficial characteristics. This will not be easy, for although there is general agreement that it will be possible to improve the efficiency of photosynthesis in plants, and Cramer (1983) suggested that there was a better than 50% chance of improving photosynthetic efficiency in plants in about ten years, there is disagreement as to how this might best be applied to obtain increases in productivity in the field.

In the UK, using current plant-breeding techniques, a higher level of photosynthetic activity has already been successfully transferred into a modern bread-making quality wheat from a more-efficient wild species. A naturalized grass species growing in the UK has also been identified as a potential source of suitable material, exhibiting rates of photosynthesis at temperatures above 15°C which are high when compared with cultivated grasses.

Grain yield and total plant dry matter

Some scientists believe that the yield of wheat and of some other crops may be limited more by deficiencies in the translocation and storage processes within the plant than by the efficiency of photosynthesis. However, it seems that as the potential yields increase, productivity will be raised through the combined effects of improvements in photosynthetic efficiency and improvements in translocation and storage in plants. Certainly, economic yields of crops could be increased by ensuring that more of the plant's total dry matter is translocated into the parts of the plant which have economic value.

The 'harvest index' of a cereal crop is the grain yield expressed as a percentage of the total plant dry matter above ground at harvest. Current wheat varieties have a harvest index of about 50%. The upper limit in the UK is probably 62% for the currently grown semi-dwarf varieties (Austin, 1980). If this were to be generally achieved, an increased grain yield of about 25% over current yields could be expected.

It is possible to increase the total dry matter production by improving the processes described above and also by changing the morphology of the plant – the leaf size and shape, the leaf angle, the leaf area and the duration of active leaf canopy. Similarly, changes in the time of flowering, lengthening the duration of the period of translocation of dry matter to the storage organs (e.g. extending the grain-filling period in cereals) can further enhance yields.

Conventional plant-breeding techniques involving the production of better-performing plants from the crossing of selected parents will continue well into the next century to produce higher-yielding varieties, with enhanced qualities and improved disease resistance. Forecasts by plant breeders (Bingham, 1981) suggest that improvements of this kind will increase the genetic yield potential of cereals by at least 1% per annum. Such forecasts may not have fully assessed the potential contribution of biotechnology over and above conventional procedures.

The contribution of biotechnology

Biotechnology, largely through gene manipulation, is able to extend the genetic variation in potential parent material by introducing single genes or multigenes from either the same or other species, by means other than sexual reproduction. This could be a very quick method of introducing and achieving genetic change and improved performance into commercial varieties.

Other developments in biotechnology, including chromosome manipulation, anther cultures, somaclonal variation and protoplast fusion, can also be expected to effect improvements in yields, both in quantity and in quality.

Although the examples discussed above relate largely to cereals and grass, there are opportunities for improvements in all crop plants, and similar developments can be expected, though the yield increases may not be equally significant.

In the assessment of yield trends in later sections it will generally be assumed that:

1. There will be no constraints either on the use of existing technology or on the uptake and use of the new technologies already identified or still to come;

2. Real prices of agricultural products and inputs will remain close to 1988 levels (though in the wider discussion the expectation of falling real prices is considered);

3. Agricultural policies will continue to provide a favourable economic environment supporting agricultural production up to the identified levels of market demand.

Improvements in the control of diseases, pests, frost damage and losses through respiration in crop production

Improvements in the performance of existing chemical pesticides and the development of new ones will contribute to improvements in productivity. Better cultural and crop management techniques, associated with increased levels of resistance to pests and diseases in the new varieties produced by conventional plant breeding, will also result in higher yields by enabling the higher potentials of the new varieties to be realized. This approach can raise yields at relatively low cost and has the advantage of being environmentally benign.

Over the past 30 years there have been improvements in plant resistance not only to diseases but also to insect damage, by the development of plants which are either unattractive to insects or have adverse effects on the insects that feed on them.

Biocontrol agents produced through biotechnology could have a major attraction as alternatives to chemical pesticides. They should make it possible to extend the range of effective and acceptable control measures. They could be highly specific, and this would be associated with minimal risks of crop damage and more effective control. They could also, where appropriate, be of low persistence. Their environmental impact could therefore be low. These biocontrol agents would be based on modified naturally occurring micro-organisms which could be used as seed treatments or as inoculants, or be released on to the crop, the soil or other elements of the environment.

Some field trials and development work using biocontrol agents to combat disease and pests are already underway. The initial results are promising. Protection of some plants from virus disease has already been achieved by inoculating the plants with a mild virus strain which has little effect on plant performance but which protects the plant against severe virus strains which would otherwise cause a substantial loss of yield.

The use of non-pathogenic micro-organisms to colonize plant surfaces (roots, leaves and stems) and to prevent infection by pathogenic organisms is already under development and test, showing particular promise in the control of root diseases and pests. It has also been demonstrated that a modified bacillus applied to leaves of early crops (e.g. strawberries and potatoes) can reduce frost damage. Ice formation depends on the presence of bacteria which have the ability to initiate the production of ice crystals. Displacing the natural populations by the same bacillus but which genetically has had the ability for ice crystal formation removed, prevents frost damage to crops.

Herbicides

Some broad spectrum herbicides have the ability to control all grass and broad-leaved weeds at low cost and with high levels of safety. Crop resistance to specific herbicides is based on single genes which have been identified, cloned and successfully transferred from resistant weeds into some crop plants. Tolerance to specific broad-spectrum herbicides has already been introduced into modern varieties of tobacco, tomatoes and petunias, so that the herbicide has no effects on the crop plant.

The advantages of herbicide-resistant crops are based on the evidence that hitherto the so-called selective herbicides may have reduced crop yields, whereas further reduction has taken place through competition from surviving resistant weeds.

The development of new selective herbicides may well remedy this situation to some extent, but the risk that populations of resistant weeds might build up is likely to remain; in the longer term, the use of broad-spectrum herbicides combined with the development of herbicide-resistant crops can be expected to gain ground.

Improvements in crop management

Matching the supply of nutrients to the needs of the crop can be achieved through changes in fertilizer technology and management. Farmers will be able to make more accurate assessments of fertilizer requirements and of the most effective timing of applications. Developments are already being made in the formulation of fertilizers, including their nutrient-release characteristics. These changes should reduce the occurrence of wasteful applications while ensuring that the realization of the yield potential of the crop is not hampered by inadequate nutrient supply.

The better use of nutrients from fertilizers and from the soil should be further enhanced by improvements in crop varieties. The addition of micro-organisms as seed dressings or to the soil may further improve the release of soil nutrients to the plant, both in amount and in timing. At present, approximately 80% of the phosphate applied as fertilizer is not taken up, being fixed in the soil in an unavailable form. Similarly, with nitrogen applied to grassland, studies at the Grassland Research Institute (Morrison *et al.*, 1980) found that only 48% of an application of 300 kg of nitrogen per hectare was recovered in the cut grass; the remainder was lost by denitrification, by leaching out of the root zone or by incorporation into the organic matter of the soil.

Improved crop management systems will come not only from advances in knowledge of the needs of the crops but also from electronic and related technologies which will enable processes to be monitored and accurately controlled so as to ensure optimum timing of operations.

Availability of nitrogen

Much attention is being given to the availability of nitrogen. Its insufficient supply is frequently the yield-limiting factor in crop production in the UK, high yield levels requiring large amounts of nitrogen. For instance, the total amount of nitrogen present in a crop of wheat yielding 13 tonnes of grain per hectare at harvest would be about 330 kg, two-thirds of this being in the grain itself.

The source of nitrogen is the air, and to be useful to plants the nitrogen gas has to be 'fixed' by converting it into a range of useful compounds. Manufacturers will no doubt be able to increase the efficiency of the fixation process and reduce its cost. Even so, the cost of the energy used in the process is a major element which seems likely to limit opportunities for price reductions of nitrogen supplied to the farmer.

The fixation of nitrogen is carried out biologically in the field by micro-organisms, but not by higher plants. Although the understanding of the basic processes and the identification of the genes involved are advancing, it seems unlikely that this capability will be successfully introduced into higher plants in the foreseeable future. Even if it is eventually achieved it will probably provide only a part of the nitrogen requirements of high-yielding crops, the remainder still having to be supplied by fertilizer.

Meanwhile, progress is being made in improving the efficiency of nitrogen-fixing micro-organisms and in establishing new symbiotic associations between them and crop plants. The crop provides the habitat and the supply of energy for the micro-organisms, while it benefits from the supply of nitrogen fixed by them. Improvements in this process will be sought, both by modifying the crop plant and by increasing the efficiency of the micro-organism in its fixation function. In legume–rhizobial associations, the use of improved strains and better-adapted host plants could result in improvements in nitrogen fixation of over 30%. In grassland, the average rate of fixation by legumes is only about 15 kg of nitrogen per hectare per year, compared with potential rates of over 300 kg per hectare.

Improvements in animal performance

Over the past 30 years the productivity of the milk and meat sectors has increased dramatically. This is attributable to the use of superior animals, higher levels of fertility and fecundity, reduction in losses from diseases and pests and improved nutrition and feeding management. For example, the average yield of milk per cow has risen from 3,700 litres in 1965 to 4,927 litres in 1988 – an average increase of 60 litres per year. In pig production, feed conversion rates have improved from 3.7 kg of feed per kg of live-weight gain in 1970 to 2.9 kg in 1987. Similarly, annual egg production per hen increased by 40% between 1960 and 1988.

As in crop production, the more widespread application of existing technology will continue to produce increases in productivity, whilst new technology should increase the potential rates of improvement substantially. Progress in providing superior animals has hitherto been made using the traditional genetic approach, and this might be expected to continue to raise productive potential in cattle and sheep at a rate of about 1% per year, though historically the rate achieved under normal farming conditions has been considerably less than this.

Using stock produced from superior sires and dams will continue to raise their productive potential, and this combined with improvements in the methods of genetic selection, in fertility and in fecundity should enable the annual rates of increase in productivity to be raised by at least 30%.

Multiple ovulation and embryo transplants

A further thrust will be given by the new techniques of multiple ovulation and embryo transplants (MOET) which can now be used in cattle, sheep and pigs. These techniques increase appreciably the reproductive rate of the dam and will make it possible to use only dams of identified superior performance. Once the nucleus herds are established, the potential rate of genetic improvement in the national herd of cattle can be expected to double.

As this MOET approach depends on a supply of fertilized eggs, the number of suitable eggs available is critical. New technology provides the techniques to increase the number of embryos from a fertilized ovum by dividing the embryos into individual cells at the two- or four-cell stage. A larger number can be produced by the transference of nuclei from identical cells in a developing embryo into recipient ova, ensuring a larger number of embryos from a single superior dam.

Ultimately it should be possible to control the sex of the embryo, or failing this, to sex embryos by immunological techniques. This would allow beef cows to receive male embryos if a twinning programme is followed, or a single female embryo if beef production is based on an all-female line. With dairy cows, on the other hand, a sufficient number would receive female embryos to provide the herd replacements, the remainder receiving male beef-type embryos, single or twins, to produce calves for beef production.

Transgenic animals

'Transgenic' animals are those which have received genes from other organisms. These may be genes derived from their own species, from other species of animals, plants or micro-organisms, or (after modification in the laboratory) from any other source. In the past the inability to achieve this has been one of the technical barriers to the production of improved livestock.

In the longer term, both genetic engineering within a species and the production of transgenic animals should widen the range of genetic variation, further enhance the genetic potential and hence increase productivity. Scientists have already produced transgenic sheep and pigs, and transgenic cattle embryos.

The production of transgenic animals with improved disease resistance and possessing specific production traits has yet to be achieved; these characteristics are controlled by several genes. However, once these improvements are achieved they will be inherited by the progeny and thus have the advantage of permanence.

Other developments

Other biotechnological developments which rely on similar genetic

engineering techniques will have a more rapid impact on animal production. These provide the ability to produce proteins, peptides and protein-
like pharmaceuticals, cheaply and on a large scale, from genetically
modified micro-organisms. These proteins and peptides are the naturally
occurring substances which regulate growth, reproduction and lactation in
animals, and can also enable improved methods to be introduced for the
diagnosis, control or treatment of disease. These developments will have
immediate and far-reaching effects on animal production through the treatment of individual animals; in the longer term the desired traits will be
transmissible genetically.

In disease control, these new technologies will provide accurate on-
farm detection kits for early diagnosis of all types of disease, and will
enable important specific control measures to be undertaken. Reproductive
inefficiencies associated with health problems are common in the UK, and
in the USA they are estimated to limit the productive capacity of farm
livestock to only 65% of their potential (US Congress OTA, 1986).

The regulation of growth, of lactation, of the composition of milk and
of the formation of meat carcasses is very important in terms of productivity. Developments in technology have already provided the scientific
methods to examine the potential of hormones in regard to these features.
It is possible to manufacture large quantities of these hormones or to
increase the supplies of naturally occurring substances which produce
similar end-results. However, these hormones and the prospect of their
widespread use have already given rise to problems of social acceptability
which have resulted in certain prohibitions, the basis of which is more
political than scientific or clinical.

Increased production of grass and forage, associated with continuing
improvements in grazing systems and in the utilization of the forage
available in various forms, will enable substantial increases in stocking rates
(i.e. the number of animals per hectare) to be achieved. Advances in
nutrition and in the understanding of digestion (in particular, rumen
function) and of the factors controlling feed intake and nutrient partition
(diverting nutrients to tissue with economic value rather than, say, to fat
production) will add further to improvements in feed conversion into
animal products. There is the possibility of modifying the bacteria in the
rumen, in kind or in performance, so as to improve feed conversion by
increasing the ability of the bacteria to digest cellulose. Similarly, it should
be possible to adjust the supply of amino acids, improve protein synthesis and
reduce losses in the digestion process (e.g. methane production in the rumen).

Timing of the introduction of new technology

At any given point in time, the impact of the commercial introduction of
new technology on productivity and on land use depends on when the

technology becomes available and on the rate of uptake. In general, the new biotechnology associated with animal production will be available for commercial use earlier than developments in plant production. A great deal of the basic research work carried out in relation to humans is immediately applicable to farm animals, and in this area the understanding, techniques and application are such as to promise early advances on the farm. Even so, there will be considerable differences in the timing of the introduction of specific developments. Genetically engineered animals with improved productive efficiency will probably become available after the year 2000; similar developments in plants will probably occur a decade later (Tables 3.1 and 3.2).

Many of the economic traits in plants, including durable disease resistance and nitrogen fixation, are under multigene control. These will take much longer to improve than the traits where only single-gene manipulation is required. Moreover, though plants are known to have a disease-immune system, methods have not yet been developed to exploit this,

Table 3.1 Approximate time schedule for the commercial introduction of animal technologies.

Genetic engineering	
Production of pharmaceuticals	1988
Control of infectious diseases	1988
Improvements in animal production	2000
Reproduction	
Fertility improvement	1990
Multiple ovulation and embryo transplants (MOET)	1990
MOET and genetic engineering	2000
Regulation of growth and development	
Hormone control of growth and production	1990
Immunological control	1995
Genetic control	2000
Nutrition and feeding	
Rumen microbiology and digestive physiology	1995
Genetic engineering improvement	2000
Grass and forage utilization	1988
Disease control	
Diagnosis	1988
New vaccines	1990
Immunology	1988
Selection for disease resistance	1995
Genetic engineering resistance	2000

'1988' signifies introduction in the years up to and including 1988.
Note: The categories used are only general groupings. There will be timing differences as between specific animal species, forms of production and diseases.

Table 3.2 Approximate time schedule for the commercial introduction of plant technologies.

Genetic engineering	
Microbial inocula	1990
Plant propagation	1988
Cereals genetically engineered	2010
Grasses and clovers genetically engineered	2010
Photosynthesis	
Breeding	2000
Genetic engineering	2010
Disease and pest control	
Genetically engineered	2005
Biocontrol agents	1990
Nitrogen fixation	
Improved rhizobia	1988
Improved legumes	2000
Cereals and mycorrhiza	2000
Cereals and grasses, nitrogen fixing	2040
Stress resistance	
Temperature	2015
Drought	2005
Fertilizer	
Increased efficiency by microbial agents	2000

'1988' signifies introduction in the years up to and including 1988.
The note relating to the schedule for animal technologies (Table 3.1) applies also to plants.

whereas in the case of animals a wide range of developments are already beginning to take effect.

Take-up of new technology by farmers

Several generations of British farmers have exhibited their willingness and ability to take up and apply technology, but since 1945 this aptitude has been particularly in evidence. This has been during a period characterized in the main by favourable prices – though these have not been maintained in recent years – and increasing market size within the context or rising UK self-sufficiency, although in part this has been sustained by the provisions for 'intervention' purchases by state authorities to remove surpluses from the Community markets. The treadmill effect described earlier has also been a strong influence in favour of technological advance, which can be seen both as a cause and as a consequence of financial pressures on farmers.

The market place is becoming more specialized and is demanding specific qualities and greater reliability and continuity of supplies. Farmers cannot expect to be able to meet these market requirements without some application of new technologies. If outlets for the sale of products are no longer to be guaranteed and market forces are to operate more freely, farmers will have an increasing interest in competing successfully for maximum market share. Farm income levels will then largely depend on achieving low unit costs of production; the most cost-effective new technologies will be at a premium.

Effects on use of farm resources

Higher levels of productivity will result in a surplus of resources relative to needs, and a new balance in resource use will be inescapable. If farmers retain these resources but use them profitably in non-agricultural activities, they should be able to maintain and even improve their incomes.

Most of the recent technological changes have necessitated increased expenditure by farmers on inputs, and have increased their capital requirements. If, on the other hand, the forthcoming new technologies are largely biological they may not give rise to much, if any, net new investment, except where extra production requires an increase in storage capacity and in associated plant and machinery.

On farms where land is taken out of production and where numbers of livestock are reduced, labour requirements will fall and investment in animals and animal housing will be on a reduced scale. Moreover, biological improvements in plant breeding and in animal selection are likely in the long run to reduce expenditure on pesticides, veterinary services and various other inputs.

In physical terms – but not necessarily in terms of current values – less working capital will be required per unit of output, owing to improved efficiency in the use of inputs and to the reduction of losses in production and marketing.

New technology and the environment

Farming is under pressure to adopt systems and production methods which are less damaging to wildlife and the environment. In general, the adoption of the new technologies identified in the foregoing sections is expected to have beneficial effects in relation to the environment.

By exploiting the higher productivity potentials of plants and animals, the area of land required for food production would be substantially reduced. As there is generally an inverse relationship between the value of land for agriculture and its suitability as a habitat for wildlife, any tendency to concentrate food production on the land with the highest production potential would release areas for less intensive uses which would be more favourable to wildlife conservation.

It is not only the intensity of the production systems which is important in this respect, but also the qualitative nature of the inputs which are used and their potential for environmental damage. The use of biological rather than chemical technologies to counter disease, by way of genetic resistance, vaccines and biocontrol of pests, could well prove to be of greater environmental significance than any reduction in the quantity of inputs on large areas of land.

New technology and agricultural structure

Agricultural structure in this context relates to types of farming; farm size; farm capital; farm tenure; and the nature and size of the industries supplying materials and services to agriculture and processing and marketing its products.

Historically, technology has provided an impetus to considerable changes in the structure of farming. In the past 40 years it has strongly encouraged and supported the specialization of production, increases in farm size and the concentration of production in fewer farms (see Chapter 1).

Prospects for large and small farms

In the future, even though much of the emerging technology will in principle be equally applicable on small and large farms, the adoption and the benefits are likely to continue to show a bias in favour of the larger businesses. These farms tend to be more alert to new opportunities. They are likely to obtain higher financial benefits from the early adoption of the technology and from the ensuing economies of scale and greater specialization. Small farms are thus likely to be at an even greater competitive disadvantage than hitherto, and unless there is massive governmental intervention in their favour their share of the market will fall. Whether their numbers will fall correspondingly will depend on the extent to which they are able to engage successfully in non-farming activities (see Chapter 9).

Another reason why the tendency for farms to become fewer and larger is unlikely to cease is that as markets become more specific in their requirements and as the food outlets to wholesalers and retailers continue to decline in number and increase in size, there will be a greater degree of co-ordination and vertical integration of production, more sales under contracts and an associated reduction in market access, all of which will provide a strong incentive to farmers to rationalize their businesses in ways which match the market's changing requirements. If biotechnology makes possible the better control of the qualities of the end-product on the farm, this will provide a further incentive to specialization and vertical integration, especially in livestock production. If the new techniques can be effectively introduced only above a certain 'threshold' size of operation, it will be very difficult for smaller-scale producers to compete.

Quality improvements on the farm

No doubt many opportunities for the improvement of food quality will be found after the product has left the farm, and biotechnology will have an important part to play in the food-processing industries. Nevertheless, quality improvements introduced on the farm to match the needs of these industries will enable farmers to enhance the added value to be obtained at the point of sale. Such an expectation does not overlook the demand for 'natural' or 'organic' foods, which appears to be gathering strength. Farmers who cater for this market are likely to be less involved than others in the introduction or extension of food-processing activities on the farm.

Changing requirements of the food industries

Some of the changes which will occur in the food-processing industries will lead to changes in the relative requirements of different kinds of farm products. For instance, an increase in the protein level of wheat flour may require increased supplies of gluten, which in turn would require a greater production of wheat than would otherwise be the case. As another instance, the food and drink industries might increase their use of iso-glucose produced from maize or wheat as a replacement for sugar, which is not only feasible but is already an economic proposition in some relative price situations. Again, microproteins produced from a cereal feedstock already replace meat in some traditional meat products, and further developments in technology could provide a wider basis for a dietary switch from animal to vegetable products – for example, milk proteins could be produced from plant materials.

Changes in farmers' inputs

Turning to the agricultural supply industries, the higher productivity of the inputs which farmers will use in the future will change the pattern of demand, and seems likely to reduce the total quantity of these inputs, unless new food markets are developed outside the UK or unless appreciable areas of agricultural land are transferred to uses other than food production but at levels of intensity comparable with the present use. Disease-resistant and pest-resistant plants and animals would have a reduced demand for chemical products.

Much of the R & D in the plant field is being carried out by private companies. Many are large and multinational, with a wide range of business interests. To ensure that private investment in R & D in this field is continued, greater protection of intellectual property rights is likely to be demanded in the biological sectors. This would mean that more of the burden of recoupment of costs would be borne by the farmers. For example, the prices of seeds might be substantially higher than at present. This could slow down the rate at which new technology would otherwise have been taken up, since farmers might choose to continue with the more conventional varieties, together with the appropriate pesticides, if these were still available.

Some implications for selected products

(Editor's note. The discussion looks ahead to the year 2015, in response to the terms of reference of a study which the author was called upon by MAFF to carry out as a research project.)

Cereal productivity from new technology

A statistical examination of historical yield data shows that yields increased exponentially between 1955 and 1985, although a linear regression also produces a reasonable correlation. The average yield actually achieved in the three-year period 1984–6 exceeded the 'expected' yields from the regression. In projecting yields to the year 2015, the base used for '1985' is this three-year average (Table 3.3).

Published estimates of maximum potential yields of winter wheat (e.g. Austin (1980) at 11.4 tonnes per hectare) are below the future average yields as projected on the statistical basis shown above. Currently the highest recorded yields under field conditions are 14.0 tonnes for winter

Table 3.3 Projected cereal yields, 2015 (tonnes per hectare).

'1985' (av. 1984–6)		2015	
		Exponential	Linear
Wheat	7.00	13.69	10.48
Barley	5.25	8.56	7.17

wheat and 12.2 tonnes for winter barley. In 1986 part of a field of wheat harvested by the East of Scotland Agricultural College (I. Beattie, personal communication) yielded 17.3 tonnes per hectare. (The whole field was not harvested under supervision, so its exact yield is not known.) Theoretically the biological potential for the yield of wheat grain and straw could be as high as 32 tonnes per hectare. At a harvest index of 60% this would produce a grain yield of 19.2 tonnes per hectare.

On the basis of the appraisal of the contributions of emerging technology to future increases in yield, it was judged that an exponential increase would not be sustained over the 30-year period. The historical linear rate of yield increase, plus 20% to accommodate the benefits of new technology, would produce a more probable yield level. It is also necessary to adjust the average yield in relation to area grown, assuming that a reduction in area would produce higher average yields, production tending to be concentrated on the higher-yielding land; and vice versa for an expansion in area (Table 3.4). Survey data have been used to quantify these adjustments. The yield levels adjusted in this way have been used subsequently in preparing the land budgets. It is a matter of personal judgement whether the law of diminishing returns will prevail and prevent yield developments of this kind.

The major factors which have contributed to yield increases in cereals over the past three decades and which are likely to continue to operate include the availability of higher-yielding varieties; improved weed, pest and disease control, and further improvements in general husbandry. The average use of nitrogen fertilizer on wheat has increased from around 90 kg in 1975 to 190 kg in 1988; to realize the average yield in 2015 of 12.8 tonnes per hectare shown in Table 3.3, the level of nitrogen fertilizer usage may be expected to increase to about 300 kg/ha. Similarly for barley, the level of nitrogen fertilizer use would rise from 127 kg/ha in 1988 to about 250 kg/ha in 2015.

Table 3.4 Projections of yield and production to 2015 on various area assumptions.

	Area million ha	Yield tonnes/ha	Production million tonnes
Wheat	2.66	10.5	28.0
	0.94	12.8	12.0
	0.83	12.9	10.6
Barley	0.51	9.8	5.0
	0.40	9.9	3.9
Oats	0.05	9.8	0.5

Grassland productivity from new technology

The current levels of output from grassland are well below the levels that could be achieved by making full use of existing technology. Cooper (1976) showed that if nutrients and water were in unlimited supply a yield of 25 tonnes of dry matter per hectare could be obtained on fertile soils. However, grassland productivity depends not only on the amount of edible material produced but also on the efficiency of its utilization. This in turn depends on the type of livestock being fed, the production system being followed, and in particular the place of grass and forage in the diet of the animals concerned.

Since 1955 the total area of grass and forage in the UK has fallen by 9%, while the numbers of grazing livestock units have increased by 39% (Table 3.5). The new technology will provide opportunities for continuing improvements in productivity at least at the historical rate, whilst improvements in animal performance will increase the potential for very high levels of land productivity in the fertile lowlands.

For the purpose of the land use budgets which follow, the likely average rates of annual improvement in grassland production and utilization have been assumed to be 2% on dairy farms, 1% on beef and sheep farms in the lowlands and 0.5% for beef and sheep in the Less Favoured Areas (LFA).

Milk production and new technology

Over the last decade the rate of increase in milk yield per cow has been around 2% per annum in England and Wales, and somewhat less in Scotland and N. Ireland. Technological developments contributing to these increases include improved genotype arising from breed substitution or selection of strains within breed, improved fertility and reproduction,

Table 3.5 Grassland area and utilization.

	1955	1970	1988
Total grassland (million ha)	14.5	13.9	12.7
Enclosed grassland (million ha)	7.8	7.2	6.8
Rough grazing (million ha)	6.7	6.7	5.9
Total livestock units (millions)	8.0	10.3	11.1
Stocking rate (livestock units/ha)	1.0	1.4	1.6
Percentage of metabolizable energy provided by grass		72	

Source: Adapted from Wilkins (1987).

reduced losses from disease, and improvements in nutrition and feeding systems.

In the future, opportunities for breed substitution will be less, but there will be continuing and greater opportunities for improvements of genotype within breeds.

The use of the multiple-ovulation and embryo-transplant techniques could very well double the rate of genotype improvement. Developments in biotechnology can improve fertility by a variety of means, whilst inefficiencies in milk production arising from losses due to disease are likely to be considerably reduced. After the year 2005, genetic engineering for improving milk production may be an additional factor.

Developments in the field of nutrition and feeding following a better understanding of the factors controlling feed intake, nutrient partition and rumen function could substantially increase milk yield per cow and improve feed conversion efficiency.

The reduction in the size of the dairy herd will also in itself tend to increase the average level of milk production per cow, as the lower-yielding cows are likely to be the first to disappear.

Genetically engineered bovine growth hormone was forecast to be commercially available in the USA by 1989; this has not happened. In experiments, milk yields have been increased by 20–40%, and might increase in normal production conditions by around 25% (Table 3.6). However, the use of this hormone may prove to be unacceptable, and in the land budgets which follow no allowance has been made for it.

With continuing improvements in pasture yield and utilization at 2% per annum, stocking rates could rise from around 1.8 cows per hectare to 3.4 cows. This would in part be achieved by increasing the amounts of compound feedingstuffs fed to each animal. In spite of improvements in the efficiency of feed conversion of forage, it will probably be necessary

Table 3.6 Probable milk yields per cow (litres).

| | Bovine growth hormone | |
	not permitted (i)	permitted (ii)
1985	4,896	4,896
1995	5,973	7,317
2005	7,275	8,919
2015	8,868	10,871

Assumptions: (i) Annual increase of 2%. (ii) Bovine growth hormone used on 20% of cows in 1991, rising in equal steps to 80% in 1994 and 90% in 1995. Expected yield enhancement, 25% per cow. This is additional to the 2% mentioned in (i).

even at low stocking rates to feed additional compound feedingstuffs in order to realize the higher milk yield potential of the improved animals.

In 1985, high-performance herds with a stocking rate of 2.2 cows per hectare and an average yield of 5,547 litres per cow obtained 83 GJ of utilized metabolizable energy (ume) per hectare from grass and forage. The national average performance was around 66 GJ. A 2% annual improvement in this would provide 120 GJ ume per hectare in the year 2015 – approximately half the theoretical potential. If all the food requirements were obtained from grass and forage, at a yield per cow of 8,900 litres, the stocking rate would be 1.6 cows per hectare. To reach the stocking rate of 3.4 cows postulated above, 2.75–3 tonnes of concentrate feed would be required per cow, as compared with 1.5 tonnes commonly fed in 1985.

Further improvements in land productivity in relation to the dairy herd as a whole would arise from a reduction in the number of replacement cows required. Currently the annual replacement rate is 25%. This could be reduced to 20% through improvements in the level of fertility, fecundity, sex determination and disease control.

Beef production and new technology

Improvements in productivity arising from further developments and application of current research may be assumed to continue at roughly the present rate, at least until 2015. Conventional breeding programmes could in theory improve the genetic potential by 1–1.5 per annum; in practice the rate of progress is much slower and will probably continue at around 0.5% per annum. The use of multiple-ovulation and embryo-transfer techniques, as and when they become economic on the farm, could increase this rate to 1%. Improvements in fertility, fecundity and the use of twinning and sex determination will also improve productivity. The potential of the bovine growth hormone or other growth hormones in meat production which are likely to become available in the next few years could, if they are acceptable, produce an immediate improvement in growth rates of about 10%. This would be additional to the on-going improvements in nutrition and feeding systems and to any reduction in losses as a result of improved disease control.

The level of beef production per hectare will depend on the production system followed, the feeds used and feeding systems adopted, the yield of utilized nutrients per hectare and the associated stocking rates. In the lowlands, if we assume a 1% per annum improvement in the average yield of nutrients and a similar rate of improvement in the performance of fattening animals, this would imply a 50% increase in stocking rates by 2015; this is without the use of growth promoters.

In the LFAs, the rate of improvement in the yield of nutrients, mainly from low-quality grazing land, cannot be expected to exceed 0.5% per annum. The present stocking rate might have increased by 24% by 2015, allowing for some improvement in feed conversion and reduced losses from disease. On the other hand, potential improvements may not be fully realizable as there is considerable pressure to reduce stocking rates and the intensity of livestock production, for environmental reasons.

Sheep production and new technology

The rate of improvement of productivity in sheep farming is generally much slower than with cattle, partly because almost 60% of the sheep population is in the LFAs, where the potential is more limited. Reproductive performance in terms of lambs per ewe is likely to increase by 25% in the lowlands and 15% in LFAs, as a result of improvements in genotype, fertility and management. It is expected that improved feed conversion will increase growth rates, and that the average carcass weights of lambs will increase by 15%, with associated improvements in quality.

Increased grassland production at a rate of 1% per annum in the lowlands and 0.5% in the LFAs, together with a reduction in the number of breeding animals required, should increase the productivity of land devoted to sheep production by 15% by 2015. This assumes that financial support for the LFAs will continue and that this will enable their proportion of the total sheep flock to be maintained at the 1985 level. If the demand for sheep meat is no greater in 2015 than in 1985, that total number will be reduced because of rising productivity per animal.

Forestry and woodlands

Current government policies and financial support measures for forestry and woodlands are aimed to be sufficient to encourage the planting of considerable new areas on land released from food production. These policies are not wholly concerned with timber production *per se*, but take into consideration wider aspects of land use relating to amenity, landscape, wildlife and employment. Opportunities will be sought to replace some of the revenue which farmers have hitherto received from using the land for food production.

Changes in forestry and woodland policies will to some extent reflect changes in the perceived needs of the population, and having regard to landscape, conservation, recreation, amenity and educational interests, particularly in relation to lowland broadleaved plantations.

Compared with most other European countries, the UK has a relatively small area of woodland, which accounts for only 9% of the land area, whereas the average in the EC is 23%. This means that the UK has a relatively low level of self-sufficiency in timber. This in itself might suggest that there is considerable scope for expansion. However, even with the decline in agricultural land values, the economic case for forestry for timber production in the UK is not convincing, and seems at best to be marginal.

How and where the balance will be struck between economic and non-economic considerations is not at all clear at the present time, and opinions differ as to the level of self-sufficiency which will be reached early in the next century. Taking into account the fact that demand has been static in the UK over the last ten years, the levels of production which may be expected from existing plantations with improved management have been variously estimated at levels of self-sufficiency ranging from 20 to 50%, compared with 10% in 1985. Similar debates continue within the EC; currently a figure of 50% is commonly quoted as the likely level of self-sufficiency for the year 2000.

Farm woodlands

Only a small part of the afforested area in the UK is associated with farming. The opportunities for achieving economic returns from farm woodland are limited; in many instances it is the landscape and amenity values which are of more importance. Estimates of the current area of farm woodlands range from 225,000 to 475,000 hectares. The Government believes that given positive management these woodlands could become self-financing and in many cases could contribute substantially more than at present to the economy of the farms in question.

The Government also considers that an increase in the area of farm woodlands would provide more diversity in the countryside. In addition to the Forestry Commission's planting grants, annual payments are proposed which would extend over 20–30 years, depending on species, location, previous use and with minimum and maximum areas for individual farms. The scheme has an initial life of three years and a limit of 36,000 hectares.

However, Government support for continued expansion in the area of traditional forestry is of greater significance in land use terms than its proposals for farm woodlands. The emphasis has shifted towards the private sector. The envisaged level of new plantings is 33,000 hectares annually, under the current strategy proposals. These are reviewed approximately every five years.

Farmers' direct interest in these schemes will depend on many factors, including the types of incentives and the fact that land planted to trees cannot quickly be returned to farming because of the control measures which operate. It will also depend on the freedom of the farmer to plant a mixture of species for differential harvesting, the intended timing of harvests and the requirements relating to the general management of the woodland. In addition, success in finding the best markets will depend on the individual farmer's initiative, as well as on his ability to provide labour and machinery with low opportunity costs, and to purchase inexpensive trees. Even so, under most systems of production and in the absence of some kind of advance payment system financed by the Government, the waiting period between planting the trees and the receipt of the first income will hold out the prospect of lower income in the short term from the farm as a whole than might otherwise have been obtained.

For some farm woodlands, various forms of coppicing to provide wood for pulping or firewood may be an attractive possibility. Traditional mixed coppices with 500–1000 stools per hectare produce the equivalent of about 2.5 tonnes per hectare of dry wood. This is an annual average based on a 15–20 year harvest period. Alder, willow, poplar and eucalyptus on a 7- to 10-year cutting cycle might produce up to 6 tonnes of dry wood per hectare per annum. These are akin to normal forest operations. The original plantings are made by using twigs. All operations can be fully mechanized. Higher densities of 4,000–10,000 stools per hectare are possible on fertile soils with reasonable moisture supplies. These can begin to be harvested three years after planting and every second year thereafter, producing juvenile wood chips amounting to 17–18 tonnes of dry wood equivalent per annum, which can be used directly for fuel, converted into gas or oil or used for particle board or pulping. These markets for chips have still to be developed in the UK.

On less fertile soils and in the uplands, wood for fuel is best produced not from coppicing but from single-stem plantations. Normally only soft woods are appropriate, with harvesting taking place 20–25 years after planting.

Agro-forestry?

The term agro-forestry denotes the possibility of combining on the same land the growing of distributed trees (50–400 per hectare) and the production of crops or the grazing of animals. This has been practised in the past in traditional UK parkland, in some orchards, and in tree plantations for matchstick production. The renewed interest in the UK arises from evidence, largely from New Zealand and Finland, which suggests that in some situations agro-forestry will be more profitable than segregated forestry and agriculture. More importantly, it would bridge the income gap between planting trees and the first harvest, as there would be crops and animals to sell. However, it would involve a higher capital investment, and little is known in the UK of the interaction between the management practices for agriculture and tree production. Preliminary studies in the UK suggest that the system would not be suitable in the hill areas, as it is doubtful whether timber of sufficiently high quality could be produced. Upland and lowland pastures show more promise for producing quality timber, but it is not known whether it will be financially worthwhile compared with segregated systems.

References

Austin, R.B. (1980) Physiological limitations to cereal yields. In: Hurd, R.G., Biscoe, P.V. and Dennis, C. (eds), *Opportunities for Increasing Crop Yields.* pp. 3–17.

Bingham, J. (1971) Plant breeding – arable crops. In: Wavering, P.F. and Cooper, J.P. (eds), *Crop Production.* Heinemann, London. pp. 273–94.

Cooper, J.P. (1976) Photosynthetic efficiency of the whole plant. In: Duckham, A.N., Jones, J.G.W. and Roberts, E.H. (eds), *Food Production and Consumption,* pp. 107–26.

Cramer, W.A. (1983) Enhancing photosynthetic efficiency. In: Yac-chi Lu (ed.), *Emerging Technologies in Agricultural Production.* USDA Co-operative State Research Service. pp. 13–25.

Morrison, J., Jackson, M.V. and Sparrow, P.E. (1980) The response of perennial ryegrass to fertiliser nitrogen in relation to climate and soil. *Technical Report no. 27,* Grassland Research Institute, UK.

US Congress, Office of Technology Assessment (1986) Technology, public policy and the changing structure of American agriculture. OTA-F-285

Wilkins, R.J. (1987) Grassland into the 21st century. In: *Farming into the 21st Century.* Norsk Hydro Fertilisers, Levington, Suffolk.

Chapter 4
Future Agricultural Land Use Patterns

John North

Introduction

Chapter 3 has shown how the productivity of land changes in response to new opportunities afforded by technology; but many other factors determine the actual patterns of land use. From one point of view, the ideal pattern of land use and land management is that which secures the highest possible attainment of perceived public good – though whether the 'public' is the population of the UK, the EC or the world as a whole is a question which seldom receives much attention. What we have come to realize in the second half of the twentieth century is that farmers' interests and the public good do not always coincide. The question of land use is now on the political agenda.

Legislation and other measures directed to the general welfare may be in the areas of agricultural and food policies, fiscal and monetary considerations, trade, environmental and social aspects, and many others. Outside the boundaries of centrally planned economies, these measures will not in themselves determine the future land use patterns; but the constraints and opportunities presented will affect the decision-making of the individual farmer in relation to his own farm business, and these individual farm decisions will, in aggregate, constitute the changes in the total pattern – its main features, its proportions, its complexity and its stability or fragility.

British farmers have generally not been slow to respond to the pressures of the 'outside world'. Even so, in trying to envisage what our future land use pattern might be, we have not attempted to consider all the changes which might emerge in other countries and relate these to UK farming. Indeed, anticipating future governmental decisions even within the EC or the UK alone would be difficult enough. Instead it is assumed in this chapter that current trends in EC policies will broadly continue and against this background a number of possible land use scenarios will be examined, some of which would require further policy decisions.

For almost the whole period of the EC's existence its policies have been orientated towards the attainment of a high level of self-sufficiency in food production and the maintenance of an economically viable rural community, with a large number of people working in agriculture and receiving incomes comparable – within national boundaries if not across the Community as a whole – to those of people working in other sectors. In these respects, the EC and its Member States have been 'protectionist' towards agriculture. However, political attitudes are changing. There is now not only a commitment to free trade within the Community by 1992, but also to a more market-orientated agriculture and to a reduction in the supply of certain products in order to bring about a better supply/demand balance. Agricultural policies must also take into consideration environmental factors. At the same time the overall budgetary cost of these policies must be restrained within limits which have been defined, after strenuous negotiation.

In the analysis which follows, no attempt has here been made to predict the course of prices in general, or of relative prices as between various agricultural products. Except where otherwise stated, 1985 prices have been assumed to continue, in real terms.

Detailed land budgets for the UK have been considered for wheat, barley, milk, cattle and sheep; in 1987 these enterprises occupied over 90% of the UK agricultural land area. It is also of importance to recognize that 76% of the agricultural area is used for the production of animal feed in its various forms.

The land budgets for the selected enterprises take account of the fact that the rates of improvement in productivity and the trends in demand vary from one enterprise to another.

Food demand in 2015

The current EC strategy for high levels of self-sufficiency in temperate foods will continue to affect the UK as a participant in the Common Agricultural Policy. The aggregate domestic demand for food will depend on the size and age-structure of the population; on changes in disposable personal incomes – which in turn depend on the rate of economic growth, and on changes in tastes and food consumption habits. Projections of the total expenditure on food at the farmgate, and of its composition, are of central importance when considering the future of agriculture and of land use.

Only a marginal increase in the number of potential consumers is likely to occur between now and 2015, as the following figures indicate:

Projected population change in UK, 1987–2016

1987	56.9 millions
2016	59.4 millions

Increase:

1987–2015	4.0%

Source of 2015 projection: Office of Population Censuses and Surveys forecast for 2015.

Agricultural land budgets produced by Wye College in 1971 and revised in 1986 showed that during the period 1965–85 the demand for food at the farmgate per head of population was static. This was in spite of an income growth of 2% per annum and an overall increase in retail expenditure on food per head of 2.2%. Edwards (1986), using income elasticities of demand for food at the farmgate in the range of 0.05–0.09, forecast an increase in demand by the year 2000 of only 1–3.3% per head. This forecast is in line with the often observed phenomenon that in an affluent society the effect of economic growth on food consumption is small. The fact that the population is ageing also contributes to the expectation of only a marginal increase in food demand per head. Taking account of the small projected increase in total population, it is thought that the aggregate demand at the farmgate will be only between 3 and 5% higher in 2015 than in 1985.

A change in the apportionment of total demand between animal and vegetable products could have an important effect on land use. Such a change could come as the result of education, assessed dietary needs or fashions in eating and in choice of foods. As it requires approximately ten times as much land to produce the same quantity of food from animal products as from crops, any *major* shift towards vegetarianism could be expected to have a significant effect on the total requirements of land for food production. However, as such changes are impossible to predict, current trends have been used to estimate future demand for the products under consideration here.

Land use budgets

Because of the large number of variables operating on the agricultural scene, both on the demand side and on the supply side, with each variable beset by its own degree of uncertainty, it would be possible to construct a large number of more or less plausible scenarios for the future use of agricultural land. In the present work, only a limited number of possible policy options has been foreseen, each being geared to the same estimates of domestic demand in 2015. Later on some consideration is given to the prospects for using farm products for industrial feedstocks, and to export possibilities.

What we have called the 'efficient' scenario, which is here applied only to cereals and milk production, reflects the results of adopting an economically efficient system. This is based on achieving the lowest unit costs of production, whilst supplying the required volumes and qualities demanded by the market. The policy to move in this direction would be based on price restraint, with prices moving towards a market-clearing level. It is accepted that to describe the lowest cost system of production as 'efficient' is to take a limited view, in that no account is taken of the environmental or social costs and benefits which might accompany the adoption of the systems and practices required to supply the market requirements at minimum cost.

In the beef and sheep sectors it could be argued that the 'efficient' solution would be to move all livestock production from the hills to the lowlands. However, even if it could be convincingly demonstrated that this would bring about a significant saving of resources of land, labour and capital, such a course is most unlikely to be pursued. The declared EC policy is to prevent any general depopulation of hill areas, and the substantial financial support which has already been given for this purpose seems likely to be maintained for many years.

Because of this constraint, only one scenario for both the beef and sheep sectors is presented. Where a reduction in livestock numbers is required to balance supply and demand, the numbers of beef animals and breeding sheep are divided between the hills and uplands (LFAs) and the lowlands by the same percentage distribution as in 1985. For this reason the only scenario adopted here is one which assumes that appropriate new technology will be taken up by hill farmers as well as in the lowlands. If a reduction in total livestock numbers appears to be called for, to balance supply and demand, it is assumed that the respective hill and lowland proportions will remain as they were in 1985. It has also been assumed, partly on economic considerations and partly on welfare grounds, that no percentage increase in meat production from intensively housed beef and sheep will occur.

The milk production scenarios include in addition to the 'efficient', three variations of an 'extensive' system. These 'extensive' scenarios are designed to make use of the appropriate areas of new technology but to maximize the area of land used to produce the market requirements. The adoption of one or other of these scenarios could involve the use of a range of policy instruments such as quotas, quantitative or fiscal constraints on the use of selected inputs and incentives such as ESA type payments or LFA support measures which would give direct encouragement to the extensive systems.

The first of the extensive scenarios explores the option of maximizing the use of grass and forage as the basis of milk production. It is identified as the 'grass forage' scenario and implies a reduction in stocking rates per hectare. The milk yield would come from grass and forage supplemented by only 360 kg of cereals per cow.

The other two extensive scenarios presuppose a policy of limiting to 150 kg the amount of nitrogen fertilizer applied per hectare, whether to protect water quality, to reduce milk supply or to maximize the use of land. Of the two, the 'restricted nitrogen' scenario aims to minimize unit costs of production, within the terms of restriction and involves the use of concentrates, whilst the 'restricted nitrogen/grass/forage' scenario maximizes the use of grass and forage, within a maximum application of 150 kg of nitrogen per hectare, 50% of the economic optimum rate. This scenario again requires 360 kg of cereals to supplement the grass and forage. The restricted nitrogen reflects the concern regarding the level of nitrate in water supplies, and the possibility of legislation or taxation to limit nitrogen fertilizer usage.

Besides the 'efficient' scenario the cereal scenarios include two levels of grain production requirements which reflect the levels of demand from the dairying systems above and at two nitrogen levels unrestricted and limited to 150 kg per hectare.

This section presents only the summary tables of the enterprise budgets and of the initial overall agricultural land use and resource requirements. The additional assumptions involved and the detailed calculations are presented in the Appendix to this chapter.

The choice of 1985 as the base year for assessing future levels of production and resource use was determined by the availability of firm statistical information across the board. As the 1985 data are used for comparative purposes only and do not affect the projections to 2015, they remain a sound base year. Any changes since 1985 which affect the projections are included in the text.

Milk production

In the dairy sector the level of supply from domestic production, which may be reached without incurring heavy financial penalties, is fixed by the EC quota system and this is assumed to be the realistic target production figure. The 2015 land budget is based on a quota of 14.05 million tonnes (Table 4.1). On the basis that new technology will produce an average milk yield of 8,900 litres per cow, the number milking cows in 2015 would be

Table 4.1 Summary of land budget and input requirements for dairying.

System	1985	2015			
		(i)	(ii)	(iii)	(iv)
Land area (million ha)	2.75	0.85	1.26	1.10	2.42
Grassland (million ha)	2.20	0.60	1.20	0.81	2.36
Cereals (million ha)	0.55	0.25	0.06	0.29	0.06
Labour man years (000)	68.0	33.1	33.1	33.1	33.1
Number of animals (millions)	4.1	2.0	2.0	2.0	2.0
Nitrogen fertilizer (000 tonnes)	450	294	455	165	362
Cereal grain (million tonnes)	3.0	3.2	0.72	3.2	0.72

Key: (i) efficient; (ii) grass/forage; (iii) restricted nitrogen; (iv) restricted nitrogen grass/forage.

1.6 million and the number of dairy herd replacements 400,000 cow equivalents.

Beef production

The actual land budget for beef will depend on the distribution of the beef herd between the lowlands and the LFA, and on the balance between the various beef production systems. As has already been stated, the distribution in percentage terms between the lowlands and the LFAs is assumed to be the same as in 1985, and also would be the percentage of meat produced intensively (Table 4.2). A budget is also shown for the situation, which is not anticipated, for the relocation of beef production in the lowlands.

Table 4.2 Resource requirements for beef production.

	1985	2015	Reduction %
Land area (million ha)	2.18	1.51	32
Grassland (million ha)	1.92	1.39	28
Cereals (million ha)	0.27	0.12	66
Labour (000 man years)	48.8	37.7	25
Number of animals (million)	5.4	4.6	15
Nitrogen fertilizer (000 tonnes)[a]	339	242	29
Cereal grain (million tonnes)	1.6	1.4	13
Alternative estimates for relocation to lowlands			
Grassland area (million ha)	1.92	1.17	40
Nitrogen fertilizer (000 tonnes)[a]	339	209	38

[a]Beef and sheep.

Sheep production

As with beef production it is assumed that the breeding flock will be distributed between the lowlands and LFA on the same percentage basis as in 1985 (Table 4.3).

The area of grass allocated to sheep can only be an estimate, particularly as in Northern Ireland and Scotland beef and sheep share the grazing.

Moving sheep production entirely into the lowlands would require an additional 470,000 hectares allocated to sheep, but this would be most unlikely (Table 4.4).

Table 4.3 Land use budget for sheep.

	Lowland		LFA		Total	
	1985	2015	1985	2015	1985	2015
Breeding sheep (million)	5.8	4.4	9.19	7.6	15.7	12.0
Lambs per ewe	1.46	1.80	1.17	1.34	—	—
Stocking rate (ewes/ha)	8.9	12.0	—	—		
Grassland area (million ha)	0.65	0.36	7.5	5.8	8.15	6.16

Table 4.4 Land budget for sheep 2015 – all in lowlands.

Breeding sheep (million)	10.0
Lambs per ewe	1.8
Stocking rate (ewes/ha)	12.0
Grassland area (million ha)	0.83

Cereals production

In estimating the demand for cereals in 2015 it has been assumed that the demand for uses other than animal feed will increase by 5% over 1985, the increase being allocated to wheat (Table 4.5). This reflects further substitution of barley by wheat and also a limited substitution of maize by wheat, for technical and economic reasons. Animal feed requirements are assumed to be in line with a reduction in the numbers of cows, sheep and cattle and have been adjusted to allow for projected improvements in animal performance. Feed grain requirements are further reduced to accommodate an expected increase in animal production from grass and forage. Pig and poultry grain requirements are maintained at the 1985 level, the increased production arising from improved animal performance and an increase in food conversion efficiency.

The future requirements for cereals for sheep and beef production are difficult to assess. Although the new technologies will provide opportunities for producing more red meat from grass, the requirements of the market are becoming more discerning in terms of carcass conformation. Carcass qualities can be improved by the use of more cereals in rations and by the use of growth regulators but the use of growth regulators are currently unacceptable. An alternative to the use of more cereals would be to reduce the fat content of grass fed meat by changing meat preparation techniques for example adopting the techniques used by butchers in Belgium, where fat is cut from the carcass during preparation for sale.

As there is the possibility that cereals may become cheaper relative to

Table 4.5 Estimated domestic demand for cereals (million tonnes).

Systems	1985	2015	
		(i)/(iii)	(ii)/(iv)
Wheat total	10.9	12.5	11.1
Animal feed	5.2	6.0	4.6
Milling	4.7	5.0	5.0
Seed	0.3	0.2	0.2
Other	0.6	1.3	1.3
From domestic production	9.6	12.0	10.6
Barley total	6.7	5.0	3.9
Animal feed	4.5	3.0	1.9
Brewing/distilling	1.7	1.7	1.7
Seed	0.3	0.1	0.1
Other	0.2	0.2	0.2
From domestic production	6.6	5.0	3.9
Oats total	0.6	0.7	0.7
Animal feed	0.4	0.4	0.4
Milling/seed/other	0.2	0.3	0.3
From domestic production	0.5	0.5	0.5
Maize total	1.4	1.2	1.2
From domestic production	0.0	0.0	0.0
Total	19.6	19.4	16.9
Animal feed	10.5	9.4	6.9
Human consumption	7.7	8.2	8.2
Other	1.4	1.8	1.8
Cereal substitutes	1.4	1.4	1.4
Total domestic demand	21.0	20.8	18.2
Total production	22.4	17.5	15.0

Key: (i) efficient; (ii) grass/forage; (iii) restricted nitrogen; (iv) restricted nitrogen grass/forage.

grass in the future, the budget has assumed an average level of cereal use per animal in 2015 similar to the levels in 1985 but adjusted for improved performance. In other words no change is anticipated in the balance of intensive and extensive red meat production systems.

The difference in cereal demand between the scenarios reflects the difference in the grain requirements between the low cost systems and systems which maximize the use of grass and forage. The total also accommodates continued imports of 500,000 tonnes of hard wheat for specialist use and expected imports of maize and cereal substitutes. The total cereal demand from home production (Table 4.5) under scenarios (i) and (iii) would be 17.5 million tonnes and 15.0 million tonnes for scenarios (ii) and (iv).

The land use budget for cereals is shown in Table 4.6.

Table 4.6 Land budgets for cereals (million ha).

Systems	1985	2015			
		(i)	(ii)	(iii)	(iv)
Wheat	1.90	0.94	0.83	1.10	0.97
Barley	1.97	0.51	0.40	0.68	0.53
Oats	0.13	0.05	0.05	0.05	0.05
Total	4.0	1.50	1.28	1.83	1.55

Key: (i) efficient; (ii) grass/forage; (iii) restricted nitrogen; (iv) restricted nitrogen grass/forage.

Agricultural land use

Table 4.7 brings together the various land use estimates made in the preceding sections. It provides an initial total land use budget for 2015 on the basis of home production sufficient to satisfy the estimated level of domestic demand at that date.

As it seems unlikely that all livestock will move from the LFAs into the lowlands, this option is not included in the table. However, even if measures are continued to support animal production in the LFAs, some movement of production towards the lowlands may take place. In terms of the impact on lowland land use, any such movement will not be very significant, as the total extra land required to replace all the LFA production would be only 510,000 ha. On the other hand, the financial consequences for the LFAs and the impact on agricultural structures would be very dramatic.

If the efficient scenario (i) was selected, the land area required to meet perceived domestic demand would be 10.6 million hectares or 60% of the 1985 area. Approximately 4.5 million hectares could be released from the lowlands and 2.5 million hectares from the LFA.

Table 4.8 includes a summary of the estimates made in the preceding sections of some of the inputs required and the reductions in unit costs which might result. These costs have been estimated on the basis that some inputs will have changed, with lower-cost cereals being used in livestock production. It has been assumed that fixed costs per ha and the prices of other purchased inputs are the same as in 1985.

Table 4.7 Initial total land use budgets (million ha).

		2015			
	1985	(i)	(ii)	(iii)	(iv)
Cereals total	4.00	1.50	1.28	1.83	1.55
Wheat	1.90	0.94	0.83	1.10	0.97
Barley	1.97	0.51	0.40	0.68	0.53
Oats	0.13	0.05	0.05	0.05	0.05
Grassland total	12.27	8.15	8.75	8.36	9.91
Dairy	2.20	0.60	1.20	0.81	2.36
Beef	1.92	1.39	1.39	1.39	1.39
Sheep	8.15	6.16	6.16	6.16	6.16
Other crops[a]	0.81	0.70	0.70	0.70	0.70
Horticulture[b]	0.21	0.21	0.21	0.21	0.21
Total[c]	17.29	10.56	10.94	11.10	12.37

Key: (i) efficient; (ii) grass/forage; (iii) restricted nitrogen; (iv) restricted nitrogen grass/forage.
[a]The area has been reduced by 14% between 1985 and 2015 to match forecast demand and to accommodate expected improvements in productivity. No allowance has been made for any net addition made by possible new crops.
[b]The area of horticulture is maintained at the 1985 level, the expected increase in demand being met by higher levels of productivity.
[c]MAFF statistics show the total agricultural area as 18.7 million. The budget given in this table excludes some common rough grazing, uncropped land and woodlands.

For beef and lamb the expected costs are expressed in relative terms (1985=100), because the wide range of production systems makes an average cost figure inappropriate. An overall reduction of 30% is assumed for these products.

At the individual farm level it may not always be possible or desirable to reduce the amounts of machinery, labour or the area of land used for food production at as fast a rate as has been estimated to apply at the national level. The aggregate of individual farm adjustments may be somewhat less than has been estimated for the national farm.

Table 4.9 derived from Table 4.8 by ranking the four different scenarios gives some indication of their relative impact on land use, nitrogen fertilizer requirements and production costs, 1 representing the greatest impact and 4 the least. It will be seen that on the whole, pursuit of the 'efficient' scenario would require the most drastic adjustment, though in terms of use of nitrogen fertilizer scenario (iii) would imply the greatest change, being explicitly designed for this purpose.

Table 4.8 Budget summary for land and other inputs and changes in unit costs of production.

System	1985	2015			
		(i)	(ii)	(iii)	(iv)
Land area (million ha)	17.29	10.56	10.94	11.10	12.37
Cereals (million ha)	4.00	1.50	1.28	1.83	1.55
Milk (million ha)	2.20	0.60	1.20	0.81	2.36
Beef (million ha)	1.92	1.39	1.39	1.39	1.39
Sheep (million ha)	8.15	6.16	6.16	6.16	6.16
Inputs					
Nitrogen fertilizer[a] (000 tonnes)	1587	1004	1164	763	952
Cereals to cattle (million tonnes)	4.6	4.6	2.1	4.6	2.1
Labour man years[b] (000)	157	83	81	85	83
Dairy animals (million)	4.7	2.0	2.0	2.0	2.0
Beef animals (million)	5.4	4.6	4.6	4.6	4.6
Sheep breeding (million)	15.7	12.0	12.0	12.0	12.0
Production costs					
Wheat (£/tonne)	98	53	53	66	66
Barley (£/tonne)	107	63	63	77	77
Milk (p/litre)	13.3	5.8	6.0	6.8	9.2
Beef (index)	100	70	70	70	70
Lamb (index)	100	70	70	70	70

Key: (i) efficient; (ii) grass/forage; (iii) restricted nitrogen; (iv) restricted nitrogen grass/forage.
[a]All crops.
[b]For cereals, milk and beef only.

Table 4.9 Environmental and economic impact.

System	(i)	(ii)	(iii)	(iv)
Land area	1	2	3	4
Cereal area	2	1	4	3
Nitrogen fertilizer	3	4	1	2
Production costs				
Milk	1	2	3	4
Cereals	1=	1=	2=	2=

Key: (i) efficient; (ii) grass/forage; (iii) restricted nitrogen; (iv) restricted nitrogen grass/forage.

Potential increases in demand from UK production

The initial land use patterns shown in Table 4.7 are designed to meet the forecast demand for indigenous products (see p. 71). As a second stage in determining probable land use patterns, it is important to take into consideration the possibilities of further import substitution, new agricultural enterprises, exports and the production of industrial raw materials on forms. These are now reviewed in turn.

Import substitution

It will be recalled that our estimated requirements of cereals made allowance for the continued importation of 0.5 million tonnes of hard wheat in uses for which home grown wheats are considered unsuitable, and of 1.4 million tonnes of maize. If developments in biotechnology make these imports unnecessary, an additional 190,000 hectares would have to be used for growing wheat in the UK.

We had also allowed for the continued importation of 1.4 million tonnes of cereal substitutes, among which manioc, maize gluten and citrus pulp are prominent. Manioc is the subject of short-term bilateral arrangements between the EC and the supplying countries, and these are constantly under review. In the event of a decision to exclude such imports into EC countries, or to put further restrictions on them, our requirements of home-grown cereals would have to be revised. As regards other kinds of cereals substitutes, there is a possibility that the need could be met, at least in part, from UK sources by utilizing the by-products of processes developed in the chemical industry which will be an outlet for home-grown cereals. The quantities involved would depend on the scale of this processing operation. At present it is difficult to judge the likely rate of growth of this new industrial use; but again there are obvious implications for the area devoted to cereals in the UK, provided our farmers can compete successfully with potential suppliers from other countries.

As regards imports of milk products, the UK has now ceased to be a net importer of butter, and, under the operation of milk quotas, it is unlikely that there is scope for any substantial further import substitution. In the case of cheese, the UK is well short of self-sufficiency, but there is a strong market demand for many of the imported cheeses and it would be surprising if consumers decided to dispense with these supplies.

The sugar supply situation is greatly affected by the undertaking to import considerable quantities from developing countries, and by the limitations imposed by EC quota arrangements. In these circumstances there appears to be no scope for any expansion in the UK sugar beet area (unless it was to supply new industrial uses), and rising yields per ha will be well able to accommodate any reversal of the downward trend in UK consumption.

New or revived agricultural enterprises

Possibilities for the expansion of various new or revived agricultural enterprises have been the subject of studies by the Centre for Agricultural Strategy at Reading (CAS, 1986). Attention was drawn to flax, peas, linseed, chickpeas, and lentils as crops for which prospects for expansion might be favourable, but the areas envisaged were relatively insignificant against the background of excess availability of land which has been presented in this section. The total expansion of area for all these crops taken together was not expected to amount to much more than 0.1 million ha.

Turning to livestock enterprises, the CAS report made suggestions which could have a more substantial impact on land use patterns. The production of feed for horses is an agricultural activity. The total number of leisure horses was estimated at 320,000 in 1983, and it is certainly increasing. This suggests that about 0.2 million ha may currently be used to supply this growing market, and the CAS study identifies a possible further increase of 0.3 million ha, mostly located close to urban areas.

There is some difficulty in handling these figures within the framework of the official agricultural statistics, because some horses are kept on land which falls outside the scope of the annual returns made by occupiers of agricultural holdings. The land which they require for grazing, riding and livery yards is not necessarily competing with other claims on 'farm' land.

However, the potential increase in the horse population is of real significance in a number of ways. Their requirements of feed (hay, dried grass and cereals) and of straw for bedding absorb agricultural resources and represent an increase in sales from the farming industry. The revenue obtained from these sales is certainly at least equal to that which would result from the same supplies being used by animals kept for food production.

Goats are another part of the livestock population which has been expanding in recent years. It is not easy to judge how far the market for their milk and their fibre might expand. Current estimates indicate that there may be some 15,000 ha being used for goat's milk production (at about 6 milking goats per ha). If liquid milk sales rose to, say, 300,000 litres, the area of land involved would still be no more than 70,000 ha; and this is probably an over-estimate because stocking rates on fully commercial farms are often higher than in the case of 'pioneers', and can be expected to increase as time goes on. Moreover, some of the sales of goat's milk will represent a displacement of cow's milk, so that the net change in land use would be of reduced significance.

A further consideration is that any expansion in the market for goat's milk would have to take place in the face of an evident increase in the interest in sheep's milk. In the CAS study the keeping of sheep mainly for milking was seen as a way of giving more productive employment to the labour available; no land use estimates were provided. In any case, the milk, wool and meat produced from the flocks in question should be seen as alternatives to the products which would otherwise have been forthcoming from more conventional flocks, or from dairy herds. Any net addition to land requirements is likely to be only marginal in amount.

More important in the context of sheep production is the possibility that wool produced from flocks in the UK might take a larger share of the home market and also find new markets abroad. At present the UK is less than 50% self-sufficient in wool. Merino sheep, which produce the finest wool, are at present less-efficient producers of meat than existing UK breeds, but research and development have already produced substantial improvements in this respect. Another possibility would be to introduce fine-wool genes into UK breeds without affecting their meat production capabilities. If developments along these lines were successful, fine-wool sheep would displace conventional flocks. The wool production enterprise might in itself become highly profitable, but the rate of increase in the total national flock would presumably be conditioned by the possibility of finding a market for the extra supplies of meat.

Much interest has been shown in the opportunities for producing mohair and cashmere fibres from goats. Quality and price will be all-important if this production is to compete successfully with imports in an open market. Goats kept for this purpose would probably be located on land of low value which is no longer needed for food production. Because of the goat's grazing habits, environmentalists would probably not wish to encourage the introduction of this enterprise into LFAs, unless they can be assured that the flocks are under constant supervision, as in some less-developed countries, so as to avoid dramatic vegetation changes and the possibility of soil erosion.

Exports

At the present time, exports from EC Member States to third countries are generally from surplus stocks, and find an outlet in other markets only because the exporters have the benefit of substantial export subsidies, or 'restitutions'. Thus the size of the future export market will be largely determined by political decisions relating to the amount of subsidy made available from Community funds. There seems to be no reason why efficient UK producers of cereals and dairy products should not be able to participate in exports if the EC persists with this kind of policy.

Exports to other Member States are also possible, but will depend on competitiveness in costs of production and transport. If the 'efficient' scenario described above was the chosen option, costs of production would be more competitive than under the scenarios which restrict nitrogen fertilizer and/or maximize the use of grassland and forage in milk production.

In the event of any substantial development in the use of cereals as industrial raw materials, potential grain exports might find themselves subjected to competition from that quarter. These industrial uses will now be further considered.

Farm-produced industrial raw materials

Historically, agriculture in the UK has produced raw materials for industry to only a limited extent – apart, of course, from materials destined for processing in the traditional food and drink industries such as milling, brewing, canning, the manufacture of dairy products, bacon factories, and sugar beet factories. In some industries, oil has taken the place of materials of agricultural origin which were previously used.

However, the position has now been reached where developments in biotechnology suggest that it may be possible for agriculture to provide carbohydrate at a price which is competitive with carbon molecules and energy derived from oil. Specifically, cereals could partly replace petroleum-based products in new fermentation processes.

There might be similar developments involving the use of potatoes and sugar. We have already remarked on the prospect that technological changes in crop production will enable supplies to be delivered from farms at lower cost than hitherto. The future pattern of crop production in the UK may be determined in no small measure by the level of these crop costs relative to oil prices – which themselves are currently determined more by factors which are broadly 'political' than by production and distribution costs.

The preferred form of the carbon molecules is currently glucose, but other sugars or starch which can easily be hydrolysed to dextrose are also suitable as feedstocks. As time goes on, developments in biotechnology will probably make all types of sugars suitable for most of the industrial processes under discussion, and will enable these sugars to be derived not only from starch and sugar but also from hemicellulose and lignin, thereby extending the range of usable agricultural raw materials to straw, wood and biomass in general.

In principle, about 95% of products derived from oil could be produced from agricultural raw materials, but relative cost is a major factor in the industrialist's choice of feedstock. Currently, 80 million tonnes of oil equivalent are used annually in the EC as chemical feedstocks. The UK's share of this is 9 million tonnes.

Many low-volume chemicals and products are already made from agricultural carbohydrate, but the quantities of raw materials involved are extremely small and have little impact on land use. The European Commission has estimated that by the year 2000, 3 million tonnes of starch will be used for industrial purposes, roughly doubling the current use of 1.9

million tonnes of cereals in the Community.

In the UK alone, according to an estimate given by the Government Chief Chemist, 1–2 million tonnes of starch will be used per annum by the year 2000; and this does not include the potentially large requirements of starch for producing plastics, nor its possible use as a source of energy.

Three other major possibilities for the industrial use of cereals and sugar are in the manufacture of polyhydroxybutyrate (PHB) to produce biodegradable plastics, the production of ethyl alcohol, and – much more speculative on economic grounds – the production of bioethanol.

Of these, the use with the most immediate potential for high volume is the production of PHB. Some of its forms are biodegradable, and if they are not too costly, cereals or sugar could replace oil in the production of plastics which are in great demand, such as polypropylene. At the present time, 3.5 tonnes of wheat are needed to produce 1 tonne of PHB.

For the production of ethyl alcohol, improved technology will be available in the 1990s. About 2.5 tonnes of wheat would produce 1 tonne of ethyl alcohol, together with 300 kg of carbonic acid, 400 kg of a high-protein animal feed (22–24% protein), and some high-quality starch. The high-protein animal feed could replace some other cereal-based feeds, beans, peas, soya beans or other vegetable proteins now being used in livestock production.

Bioethanol can be used as a substitute for petroleum spirit, but there are doubts about the cost-effectiveness of wheat or other agricultural products as a source of carbohydrate for this purpose. Apart from the costs of any raw materials, the manufacturing costs are estimated to be about £150 per tonne. Assuming that the price of wheat in 2015 will be £70 per tonne in real terms and that the animal feed produced will be worth £35 per tonne, the net cost of producing the bio-ethanol would be about £290 per tonne. As bioethanol has only 65% of the energy of petrol, this cost in terms of petrol-equivalent would be nearly £450 per tonne. The current price of petrol in Europe (before tax) is about £207 per tonne (Oct. 1989).

Summary: probable land use for agriculture in 2015

It is very clear, from the review of impending technological changes in agriculture and their implications of a reduced requirement of land to produce a given quality of food, that a challenge exists here and now for major adjustments of policy, as well as of plans for the pattern of land use on individual farms.

If policies in the coming years reflect a preference for the 'efficient' scenario, the prospects considered above for exports and for home industrial uses might increase total demand for UK cereals to 25.5 million tonnes in 1995, 28.5 million tonnes in 2005 and 33.5 million tonnes in 2015 (Table 4.10). Conversely, on the 'extensive' option, which would preclude the achievement of minimum costs per tonne, the demand might be only 16 million tonnes, unless prices of cereals for export and for industrial use were to be subsidized.

Alternative policies for dairying, in terms of cow numbers and land use, are shown in Table 4.11. The grass/forage scenario has been selected as the approach most likely to be chosen by producers. A move to the extreme extensive system, with restricted nitrogen and grass/forage feeding, is unlikely as this would require an increase in the grassland area of individual farms to accommodate the very low stocking rates envisaged.

If non-economic considerations are to weigh heavily in the balance, and the policies pursued do not give the highest priority to the adoption of the latest technology so as to reduce costs per tonne while maintaining or improving the quality of the products, this would represent a sacrifice of some promising market opportunities. If at the same time other countries, whether through active government policies or under conditions of free operation of market forces, push on in the directions indicated by their own least-cost scenario, the gap between British agriculture's performance and its full potential will widen.

The strength of the underlying economic forces which shape the whole structure and resource-use pattern can hardly be denied. The visual and statistical evidence of the operation of those forces cannot fail to impress. If they are indeed irresistible in the long run, then policy options which

Table 4.10 Cereals: alternative possibilities.

	Demand (million tonnes)	Area (million ha)	Demand (million tonnes)	Area (million ha)
1985	22.5	4.00	22.5	4.00
	Extensive policy		Efficient policy	
1995	17.3	2.20	25.5	3.18
2005	16.6	1.88	28.5	2.96
2015	16.0	1.55	33.5	3.22

Table 4.11 Dairying: alternative possibilities.

	No. of cows (million)	Land area (million ha)	Land area (million ha)
1985		3.10	2.20	2.20
	Efficient scenario		Grass/forage scenario	
1995	2.38	1.80	1.23
2005	1.95	1.47	0.84
2015	1.60	1.20	0.60

deliberately reject or substantially modify the 'least-cost' option may eventually be seen as only having delayed the adjustments which the economic forces will surely impose.

In Table 4.12 showing prospective land use, the figures for the 'efficient' scenario allow for some import substitution and the expansion of some sectors of livestock and cereals production in response to the lower unit costs, especially of cereals.

Table 4.12 Agricultural land use in 2015.

	'Extensive' scenario (million ha)	'Efficient' scenario (million ha)
Cereals	1.55	3.22
Grassland	9.91	8.15
for milk	2.36	0.60
for beef	1.39	1.39
for sheep	6.16	6.16
Other crops	0.70	0.70
Horticulture	0.21	0.21
Total requirement	12.37	12.28
Total available (1985)	17.29	17.29
Surplus (to be diverted to non-food uses or to be taken out of use)	4.92	5.01

In both of the scenarios about 5 million hectares would be released from agricultural use by 2015. Probably this would come from the lowlands and from the hills and uplands in about equal proportions.

Table 4.12 shows the consequence of the adoption of the two contrasting policies in terms of land use. Recent policy developments in the UK and EC are attempting to combine price restraint measures, tending towards the 'efficient' scenario and measures of extensification in part to keep the UK countryside as a farmscape and to leave the land under the management of farmers. This will produce a polarization whereby some land or some farms will become agriculturally more intensive, the remainder moving towards an extensive form of land use.

References

CAS (1986) Land-use alternatives for UK Agriculture. Rep. No.12. Centre for Agricultural Strategy, University of Reading.

Edwards, A. (1986) An Agricultural Land Budget for the UK. Wye College Department of Environment Studies and Countryside Planning Working Paper No. 2.

House of Lords (1987) Biotechnology in the Community. Select Committee on the European Communities.

Murphy, M. (1986) *Report on Farming in the Eastern Counties of England*, University of Cambridge.

Appendix

(Supplementary details, based on the assumptions indicated in the chapter or stated below.)

Milk Production

Table 4.13 Land budgets for dairying (000 hectares).

	1985	2015 scenarios			
		(i)	(ii)	(iii)	(iv)
Grassland	2,200	600	1,200	810	2,360
Cereals	550	250	56	293	56
Total	2,750	850	1,256	1,103	2,416

Key to scenarios: (i) efficient; (ii) grass/forage; (iii) restricted nitrogen; (iv) restricted nitrogen grass/forage.

Table 4.14 Stocking and nitrogen fertilizer rates.

	1985	2015 scenarios			
		(i)	(ii)	(iii)	(iv)
Cows ha grassland	1.8	3.4	1.6	2.4	0.8
Followers/ha grassland[a]	2.0	3.9	2.0	2.8	1.1
Nitrogen (kg/ha)					
On cereals	190	300	300	150	150
On grass	200	365	365	150	150
average	198	346	362	150	150

[a]Cow equivalents.

The effect of reducing the nitrogen rate from the optimum to 150 kg/ha would be to reduce the output of grass from 120 to 60 GJ of ume/ha, with consequent reductions in stocking rates.

Taking account of the areas of grassland and of cereals to be treated and the rates of application per ha in each case, the total requirements would be as shown in Table 4.15. The grass/forage scenarios (ii) and (iv) require, on average, 78% more nitrogen than in the average of the other two systems – an additional 178,000 tonnes. This is in contrast to the view that a more extensive use of grass would reduce total nitrogen usage.

On the assumption of quota-restricted supply, improvements in productivity will reduce not only the total number of dairy animals required but also the amount of labour (Table 4.16). Assuming a marginal improvement in labour use per cow by 2015, the total labour requirements would fall by 34,900 man-years, or just over 50%.

It is important to keep in mind that even with the assumption that the yield per cow would be the same under each scenario, at 8,900 litres per annum, the systems of milk production envisaged would give rise to a wide range of costs per cow and per litre of milk. Estimates of these costs depend substantially on the method used for allocating fixed costs. In Table 4.17 it has been assumed that two-thirds of the fixed costs are related to land area – hence the higher figures for scenarios (ii) and (iv). The figures for variable costs reflect differences in concentrate usage. It is assumed that concentrate prices will be directly related to the costs of producing cereals.

Table 4.15 Nitrogen fertilizer use in dairying (tonnes), 2015.

| | Scenarios | | | |
	(i)	(ii)	(iii)	(iv)
For grassland	219,000	438,000	121,500	354,000
For cereals	75,000	16,800	43,950	8,400
Total	294,000	454,800	165,450	362,400

Table 4.16 Labour requirements for milk production.

| | Cows | | Followers | | Total | |
	1985	2015	1985	2015	1985	2015
SMD/animal	5.0	4.8	1.5	1.5		
No. of animals (million)	3.1	1.6	1.0	0.4		
Man-years (000)	62.0	30.7	6.0	2.4	68.0	33.1

SMD: 250 standard man-days = 1 man-year.

Table 4.17 Milk production costs.

	1985	2015 scenarios			
		(i)	(ii)	(iii)	(iv)
Variable costs (£/cow)	327	295	180	332	224
Fixed costs (£/cow)	327	225	354	273	598
Total	654	520	534	605	822
Costs per litre (p)	13.3	5.8	6.0	6.8	9.2

Beef production

The forecast improvement in productivity in terms of rate of liveweight gain per beef animal is between 35 and 40%, associated with a 25% improvement in meat yield per animal. In 1985, 78% of the fattening cattle were in the lowlands, and the total number of slaughterings required for the supply of the 1985 offtake of 1.1 million tonnes was 4.2 million animals. In 2015, with the new technology, the same level of production would require only 3.3 million animals. The dairy herd of 1.6 million cows plus 400,000 replacement animals would produce a total of 1.9 million calves. Assuming a 10% calf mortality and a 20% replacement rate into the dairy herd, approximately 1.3 million calves would be available from the dairy herd, plus 300,000 cull cows, leaving a requirement of 2.0 million calves from the beef breeding herd. If the assumption of 60% twinning in 2015 proves to be correct, a beef breeding cow herd of around 1.3 million cows will be required, as shown in Table 4.18

The actual land budget will depend on the distribution of the beef herd between the lowlands and the LFAs, and on the balance between the various beef production systems. As has already been stated, the distribution in percentage terms between the lowlands and the LFA is assumed to be the same as in 1985, as also would be the percentage of meat produced intensively. Improvements in grassland productivity and in the utilization of grass and forage would suggest typical stocking rates as shown in Table 4.19.

In addition to grass and forage, the beef herd would consume approximately 1.4 million tonnes of cereals in 2015. Assuming that this would consist of 400,000 tonnes of barley and 1 million tonnes of wheat, the total land area for beef production in 2015 is shown in Table 4.20.

The estimated labour requirements, based on the 18-month beef production system as the typical fattening programme, are shown in Table 4.21. The reduction in labour use is attributed partly to a small increase in

Table 4.18 Beef herd numbers and distribution.

	1985		2015	
	Lowland	LFA	Lowland	LFA
		number of animals (million)		
Fattening cattle	3.30	0.80	2.64	0.66
Breeding cows	0.52	0.78	0.52	0.78
Total	3.82	1.58	3.16	1.44

Table 4.19 Stocking rates and grassland requirements in beef production.

	Number of animals (million)		Av. stocking rate (animals/ha)		Grassland area (million ha)	
	1985	2015	1985	2015	1985	2015
Fattening animals[a]	4.1	3.3	3.7	4.1	1.11	0.80
Breeding cows	1.3	1.3	1.6	2.2	0.81	0.59
Total	5.4	4.6	2.8	3.3	1.92	1.39

[a]Including cull cows.

Table 4.20 Land budget for beef production.

	1985	2015
	(000 ha)	
Grassland	1,920	1,390
Cereals[a]	266	115
Total	2,186	1,505

[a]Grown at optimum nitrogen rates.

labour productivity, but mainly to a 23% reduction in the number of animals.

If all beef production is switched to the lowlands (see p. 74), the area of grassland used in the lowlands increases by 40,000 ha to compensate for a release of 62,000 ha in the LFA, as shown in Table 4.22, where the figure of 1.17 million ha may be compared with 1.39 million ha in Table 4.20.

Table 4.21 Labour requirements for beef production.

	1985	2015
Breeding cows		
SMD/cow	1.5	1.4
No. of cows (million)	1.3	1.3
Man-years (000)	7.8	7.3
Fattening cattle (18-months beef)		
SMD/animal	2.5	2.3
No. of animals (million)	4.1	3.3
Man-years (000)	41.0	30.4
Total man-years (000)	48.8	37.7

Table 4.22 Land budget for beef production if all in lowlands, 2015.

	Number of animals (million)	Av. stocking rate (animals/ha)	Grassland area (million ha)
Fattening animals[a]	3.3	4.6	0.71
Breeding cows	1.3	2.8	0.46
Total	4.6	3.9	1.17

[a]Including cull cows.

As there are many different beef production systems it is impossible to produce here a budget of comparative costs similar to that given for dairying on p. 89. However, Table 4.2 shows the reductions by 2015 in inputs of land, labour, cereal grain and nitrogen fertilizer for the national beef enterprise. Overall, a 30% reduction in unit costs could be expected.

Sheep production

The current trend is a reduction in the domestic consumption of mutton and lamb, and if this continues the demand in 2015 would be 84% of the 1985 quantity. The total new supply (production plus imports minus exports) in 1985 was around 410,000 tonnes, and some 3 million lambs or carcases were exported. The average lamb carcase weight was 19.5 kg.

The anticipated domestic demand in 2015 is 350,000 tonnes. By that time technological improvements should provide a 15% increase in average carcase weight, and increases in the number of lambs produced per ewe estimated at 25% in the lowlands and 15% in the LFAs (Table 4.23).

The area of grass allocated to sheep can only be a rough estimate, particularly as in Northern Ireland and in Scotland cattle and sheep often share the grazing.

Labour and cost savings would be related mainly to the reduction in the number of sheep, which Table 4.23 shows to be 24%. Overall a 30% saving in unit costs might be expected by 2015.

Moving sheep production entirely into the lowlands – which is most unlikely – would require an additional 470,000 ha of grassland in lowland areas, to compensate for the loss of 5.8 million ha in the LFAs.

Table 4.23 Land use budget for sheep.

	Lowland		LFA		Total	
	1985	2015	1985	2015	1985	2015
Breeding sheep (million)	5.8	4.4	9.9	7.6	15.7	12.0
Lambs per ewe	1.46	1.80	1.17	1.34	1.28	1.31
Stocking rate (ewes/ha)	8.9	12.0	1.3	1.3	1.93	1.95
Grassland area (million ha)	0.65	0.36	7.5	5.8	8.15	6.16

Cereals production

The total quantities of nitrogen required for cereal production are shown in Table 4.24.

It is expected that labour inputs per ha will be lower in future (Table 4.25), resulting from a reduction in the number of field operations, e.g. in spraying, and from the availability of higher outputs per machine.

The estimated costs of production of wheat in 2015 are shown in Table 4.26. They ignore reductions in labour costs and assume that all fixed costs remain unchanged.

Table 4.24 Use of nitrogen fertilizer for cereals.

		2015 scenarios			
	1985	(i)	(ii)	(iii)	(iv)
			(000 tonnes)		
Wheat	380	282	249	165	145
Barley	260	129	103	102	79
Oats	26	7	7	7	7
Total	666	418	359	274	231

Table 4.25 Labour requirements for cereals.

| | 1985 | 2015 scenarios | | | |
		(i)	(ii)	(iii)	(iv)
SMD/ha	2.5	2.0	2.0	2.0	2.0
Area (million ha)	4.00	1.50	1.28	1.83	1.55
Man-years (000)	40.0	12.0	10.2	14.6	12.4

Table 4.26 Estimated costs of wheat production in 2015.

	Using 300 kg N per ha	Using 150 kg N per ha
Yield per ha (tonnes)	12.8	9.5
Variable costs (£ per ha)		
Seed	66	66
Fertilizers	175	114
Sprays	28	28
Miscellaneous	7	7
Total variable costs	276	215
Fixed costs	409	409
Total costs	685	624
Cost per tonne (£)	53	66

Source: Adapted from 1985 costs (Murphy, 1986).

The estimated costs for growing a hectare of barley in 2015 (at 1985 prices) are 10% below those of wheat, but with a lower yield level the costs per tonne would continue to be higher than for wheat. For the 'no nitrogen limit' scenario, barley costs are estimated at £63 per tonne, and with a limit of 150 kg N per ha, £77 per tonne. In 1985, average costs for wheat were £98 per tonne and for barley £107 per tonne.

Chapter 5
Conflict or Consensus over Agricultural and Countryside Issues?

Ian Hodge

Rural land in a changing context

Agriculture and forestry are the dominant and traditional uses of rural land. Other uses which are primarily neither for agriculture nor forestry comprise a tiny fraction of the total area: golf courses, nature reserves, grazing for ponies. Grouse moors might also be included. Accurate statistics are lacking, but the proportion seems likely to be considerably less than 5%. This means that the bulk of the demand for outdoor recreation, nature conservation and landscape amenity as well as for water gathering, must be satisfied from land which is primarily managed for agriculture. This necessarily leads to a discussion of multiple land use.

The use of a single area of land for more than one activity raises the problems of conflicts between activities. But conflicts also emerge where different uses are undertaken in close proximity. The matrix in Table 5.1 illustrates some possible conflicts between various uses of the countryside. Possible beneficial relationships are not considered. The list is not complete and could be considerably extended and refined. In particular, some uses, especially forestry, are not included and this approach fails to do justice to some of the longer-term concerns and more complex relationships. However, the uses included represent the range of activities which take place in much of the British countryside. Land uses causing conflicts are listed across the top and those which are affected are listed down the side. Inevitably there are some major impacts whereas others are of doubtful significance. It is difficult to assess the importance of the impacts involved other than in subjective terms. Generally, agriculture and urban development probably constitute the major activities causing impacts, and wildlife conservation and landscape appreciation are the most susceptible. While the impacts on these two uses result primarily from a physical change in the environment, the impacts on residential use are often of a socio-economic nature. This applies, for instance, where the popularity of an area produces higher house prices, either for first or second homes, or where it encourages immigration and pressures for new development, which threaten the character of the existing settlement.

Some assessment of the public view of the threats to the countryside

Table 5.1 Illustrative conflicts between rural land interests.

Land uses affected	Land uses causing conflict				
	Agriculture	Outdoor recreation	Wildlife conservation	Landscape appreciation	Residential uses/ urban development
Agriculture	straying animals; spray drift; resource depletion	dogs worrying sheep; damage to crops and fences; hunting	crop pests; disease transfer	constraints on farming	urban fringe problems; loss of land
Outdoor recreation	obstructing foot paths	congestion at popular sites; noisy sports	mosquitoes	encourages congestion in attractive areas	new development
Wildlife conservation	loss of habitat; isolation of remaining habitat	damage to habitat	changed ecological balance	encourages recreation	development of sites of conservation value
Landscape appreciation	loss of landscape features	damage to scenic areas	unattractive habitats	encourages congestion	urban intrusion
Residential uses/urban development	water pollution; spray drift; smells; noise; smoke	spray intruders to 'rural peace'; noise	disease risks	higher house prices; pressures for development	resentment of new immigrants; effects of development on local character

can be found in the annual survey of British Social Attitudes, referred to earlier. The survey conducted in 1987 asked respondents to choose from among seven specific items which represented, for them, the greatest threat and which the next greatest threat. The results are given in Table 5.2.

Industrial pollution was seen as the greatest threat, ahead of the use of chemicals and pesticides in farming. After these, urban development, removal of landscape and roads were ranked very closely together. Perhaps, surprisingly, litter also receives a similar ranking. Tourism and visitors were generally not seen as a threat to the countryside. There has been little change in the responses to this question since it was first asked in 1985.

These results contrast with the emphasis of the political and public debate which seems to give greater attention to the issues of loss of landscape and urban development. Tourism too is often regarded as an important threat. Nevertheless, they are similar to the results of an NFU survey conducted in 1983 (Worth, 1984), where respondents were asked what they thought was the biggest threat. Urban expansion (23%) and pollution (21%) were seen as most important. Use of chemicals/pesticides (13%) and vandalism/litter (13%) were ranked next, with cutting down hedges and trees (7%) being the least often chosen. These results show that, despite the publicity given to the impacts of agriculture in rural areas, the general public continues to perceive urban-based threats as more significant.

The determinants of conflict

What factors influence the extent to which the different activities and uses are in conflict? This depends both upon the intensity and manner by which

Table 5.2 Sources of threat to the countryside[a].

	Greatest threat %	Next greatest threat %
1. Industrial pollution	32	21
2. Motorways and road building	11	11
3. Urban growth and housing development	16	12
4. Removal by farmers of traditional landscape such as hedgerows, woodlands	11	12
5. Use of chemicals and pesticides in farming	18	26
6. Tourism and visitors	1	2
7. Litter	9	12

Source: Young (1988).
[a]Survey conducted in 1987.

they are undertaken and upon the views taken as to their impacts. And there is, of course, substantial regional variation. The activities outlined in Table 5.1 are essentially associated with three different groupings of interest: agriculture, conservation and urban development. As was mentioned earlier, until relatively recently, agriculture and conservation had been seen as being complementary. However, they are increasingly coming into conflict.

The agricultural impact

Much has been written about changes in agricultural production and these trends have been the subject of an earlier discussion. Even if not reflected in opinion polls, many writers now regard agriculture as the major threat to the countryside. For instance, Shoard (1980), an outspoken critic of agricultural change, commented that

> . . . the English landscape is under sentence of death. Indeed the sentence is already being carried out. The executioner is not the industrialist or the property speculator, whose activities have touched only the fringes of our countryside. Instead it is the figure traditionally viewed as the custodian of the rural scene – the farmer.

Official bodies have made similar, if less extravagant, claims. For instance, the Nature Conservancy Council (1984) commented that 'recent economic forces and government policy for agriculture have led to practices highly inimical to the conservation of nature.' A wide range of problems has been identified, including the destruction of representative ecosystems and individual species, the loss of the amenity value of the landscape, nitrate and other chemical pollution of water supplies, eutrophication of watercourses, nuisance from intensive livestock production, straw burning and soil erosion.

In 1984 the Nature Conservancy Council produced some stark statistics on the extent of the impact which agriculture has had on the environment since 1947. They estimated that 95% of the herb-rich meadows had been destroyed. Similarly, 30–50% of ancient lowland woods comprising mature broadleaved trees had been destroyed. Again, about 50% of wetland areas in the lowlands had been lost to drainage and reclamation.

The landscape has also undergone substantial change. Figures produced by the Countryside Commission show that in England and Wales, the length of hedgerows diminished by about 109,000 miles between 1947 and 1985. That represents about 22% of the original length. Furthermore, the annual rate of loss between 1980 and 1985 of 4,000 miles was nearly 50% higher than the average rate of loss between 1947 and 1980.

Water pollution has received considerable publicity amidst the debate over water privatization and the action of the European Commission over water quality standards. Britain is accused of failing to meet the standards laid down in a European Directive, the main problem being nitrate levels in excess of the 50 mg per litre limit. While some uncertainty remains about the details of the processes involved, agricultural change is the major factor. Less widely reported is the increase in water pollution from farm wastes. The number of water pollution incidents rose by 280% between 1979 and 1988. About 20% of the incidents in 1988 arose from silage waste, and over 50% from incidents involving dairy and cattle wastes. Other types of impact have also caused concern, such as the consequences of pesticide use, straw burning and soil erosion.

The major factor behind these impacts is the changing structure of agricultural production (Munton, 1983). Under the influences of changing prices and technology, farming has become more specialized and concentrated into larger units. With the larger scale of operation and larger machines, farmers have faced considerable incentives to increase field size by removing landscape features. Large, intensive livestock units face particular problems of effluent disposal. Increasingly, profit maximizing behaviour has led to higher levels of fertilizer and chemical use, reinforced by a move away from mixed farming. The generally more intensive use of land and, in many parts of the country, the higher proportion of land under cultivation have increased the potential damage caused. New types of owners and managers have emerged, particularly institutional owners and salaried managers, who have been identified as being least sympathetic to conservation (Newby et al., 1977).

These trends have been accelerated by the Common Agricultural Policy (CAP), which has held prices above their levels in world markets (Bowers and Cheshire, 1983). Higher prices have raised the opportunity cost of land which is not directly productive in narrow agricultural terms. They have, similarly, raised the optimal levels of use of fertilizers and chemicals and increased optimal stocking rates. Higher profits have accelerated investment in machinery and the rate of change. Over certain periods grant aid has been provided for removal of landscape features. Headage payments have encouraged higher levels of livestock production.

On the other hand, it is possible that the CAP has had some beneficial impact. For instance, higher prices might have enabled some 'traditional' farmers to remain in business while using lower levels of purchased inputs and higher amounts of labour than more 'active' farmers, thereby maintaining small islands of conservation interest which might have been lost under a more severe price environment. Further, areas of land have no doubt been farmed which would otherwise have become derelict. But the extent of this must be small in relation to the negative impacts.

The rise of the conservation interest

Although growth of the extent of concern for the conservation of the countryside is difficult to measure directly, it has found expression in a variety of changes, particularly the extent of recreational use of rural areas, the membership of and participation in associated groups and the extent of discussion of the topic which is evident in the media. In terms of the number of recreational visits to the countryside, it has been estimated that about 85% of the population visits the countryside at some time during the year. On a summer Sunday up to 18 million people are out in the country-side. Nearly 40% of these visits are for drives, outings, picnics and long walks (Countryside Commission, 1987).

There have been a number of periods in the past hundred years during which environmental groups have been established (Lowe and Goyder, 1983). The first of these was from the mid-1880s to the turn of the century, when groups such as the National Trust and the Royal Society for the Protection of Birds were founded. A second period in the middle inter-war years saw the formation of the Ramblers' Association, the Ancient Monuments Society and the Council for the Preservation of Rural England. The recent expansion began in the late 1950s, although the membership statistics showed no dramatic increase until the 1970s. Some figures illustrating the growth in membership are shown in Table 5.3.

This growth of membership is linked to the rising level of prominence given to environmental issues and to the perceptions of environmental threat. The extent to which these trends are attributable to an underlying shift of values is not easy to ascertain. One theme (Lowe and Rüdig, 1986) has been the possible development of 'post-materialist' values. This concerns a shift away from economic and base security values, towards an increasing emphasis upon 'high order' needs, including environmental values. However, Lowe and Rüdig, (1986) have argued that, despite variations expressed in the degree of concern, there appears to have been a

Table 5.3 Membership of countryside organizations.

	1950	1970	1977	1984	1988
Country Nature Conservation Trusts	800	57,000	115,000	155,000	204,000
Royal Society for the Protection of Birds	6,800[a]	65,600	244,800	380,000	540,000
National Trust	23,400	226,200	613,100	1,194,000	1,600,000
Ramblers' Association	8,800	22,200	29,500	44,000	64,000

Source: Green (1985), Barkham (1989), Ramblers' Association.
[a] 1955.

relative stability of attitudes to environmental protection. The formation of values cannot be examined in isolation from the context and issues faced.

Change in the village

Changing social and economic conditions have also tended to bring those most concerned for the amenity of the countryside into closer contact with those directly involved with its management. Since the Second World War, there has been a steady growth in income levels together with a general increase in leisure time. Combined with the rising level of car ownership and improved road network, these changes have broadened the opportunities faced by a large component of the population. This has both enabled people living in towns to gain access to the countryside for recreation and enabled people working in towns to live in the surrounding countryside. At the same time, there has been an increase in employment in small towns and rural areas. Both jobs and people have decentralized to the countryside.

As a result, the composition of the population living in rural settlements has changed dramatically. Russell (1986) and Newby (1987) have described the origins and contemporary character of social life in rural areas. The long-established phenomenon of rural depopulation has undergone a widespread reversal across a considerable area of rural Britain. This was clearly documented in the 1981 census, although there is earlier evidence of similar trends in the previous 20 years. This is not just an overspill of population into urban fringe areas, but a substantial shift of population, in association with a parallel shift of employment, into large numbers of towns and villages. The resulting pattern of population change is complex and there are many elements involved. First, it should be noted that the loss of traditional rural employment has continued often masked by other changes. In some areas which have not experienced offsetting immigration, the overall process of depopulation and decline has likewise continued. Some population growth is caused by people moving in association with the movement of employment. Other growth is caused by retirement migration, especially to the coastal and more attractive parts of inland Britain. Again, some movement is caused by an extension of commuting, often facilitated by improvements in road and rail transport. Numerous other influences cause local variations, such as changes in the location of central and local government employment, relocation of armed service bases, growth and decline of major employers in the energy sector, and so on. No single factor can explain the complex changes which have occurred. The pattern is also complex at the local level. Population has tended to concentrate in the larger settlements, while decline has continued in the smallest villages.

These changes have in turn changed the social composition of rural

Britain. Newby (1985) has written a detailed account of the changed social structure. Without undue simplification, conflict can be portrayed as between the 'newcomers' and 'locals'. The newcomers to rural areas tend to be relatively affluent, highly educated and from an urban background. They move to rural areas by choice, with the intention of enjoying the advantages of rural life. They are thus seeking an element of community in a small settlement and, especially, an attractive environment. Both of these may be based on a somewhat idealized view of what rural life should be like. However, because of their income levels and their mobility, unless they live in the remoter parts of the country, they are not required to sacrifice the comforts and convenience of urban life either. They can continue to visit local towns for the supermarkets, specialist shops and entertainment which the village cannot provide.

Once established in the rural community, the newcomer soon takes an active part in defending those aspects of it which are valued. In practice, this means a reaction against most change. In particular, threats from agriculture or from housing development are actively resisted. This may bring the newcomer into open conflict with local farmers or with others whose interests involve some element of change. At the same time, the experience and background of the newcomer frequently places him in a position whereby he is able to influence events through the planning system and the local media in a way which the locals seldom achieve. It should not be inferred from this that the newcomers make no positive contribution to rural life. On the contrary, they are active in initiating and running many community activities. But their presence shifts the balance in local debate away from those who have lived longer in rural areas and have closer attachments with the rural economy.

This movement towards small towns and rural areas itself creates new pressures for housing and industrial development in rural areas. While the newcomers may actively resist it, development will be supported by those wishing to move in and by locals wanting new employment opportunities and housing, especially at the lower end of the market. House prices in rural areas often reach levels comparable with those in urban areas and well beyond the capacity of those earning low or even moderate incomes. For instance, in South Cambridgeshire in July 1988 less than 3.5% of properties advertised were priced below £60,000. Coupled with a decline in council housing and limited housing available for private rental, access to the housing market is extremely constrained.

There are therefore considerable pressures for new development, especially in the parts of the country experiencing the highest rates of economic and population growth. These issues are fought out both at the local level over individual planning applications and over local planning policies and at the national level over policies towards development in rural areas. The latter is typically focused on Department of Environment guidance to local authorities and on Green Belt policy.

Scope for compromise

Is the conflict between farm and non-farm interests now inevitable? There is some evidence that compromise is possible in at least some respects, as well as a growing recognition that there are common interests between the agricultural and conservation lobbies in advancing their causes.

One possible approach towards avoiding conflict lies in the segregation of land uses. It would be possible to set aside some areas of land purely for conservation purposes and other areas where agriculture would take full control. Some proponents argue that, because of the differing objectives of the farmer and the conservationist, some degree of polarization is needed (Green, 1988). To a limited extent the segregation of land uses is practised – deliberately in respect of some nature reserves and by default as a result of neglect on some agricultural areas. However, many of the countryside values are dependent upon a continuation of agricultural production in a particular form. Thus, wetland habitats and upland pastures depend upon a particular grazing regime. While the abandonment of areas of land would satisfy some conservationists, it would not provide an acceptable solution to the majority of those with an interest in the countryside. In this respect, compromise is not only desirable, it is essential.

Therefore, the options available depend upon the particular environmental context, the type of agriculture practised and the conservation values involved. Where environmental values depend upon a particular type of agricultural system, and where this is not the system which generates the highest financial rate of return, then policy intervention in some form will be required if the values are to be maintained. Thus, management agreements and farmer participation in Environmentally Sensitive Areas achieve this type of objective by providing compensation to the farmers involved. Beyond these areas, in what is sometimes termed the 'wider countryside', the maintenance and development of countryside value can sometimes be advanced by means of relatively minor investments and changes to farm practices.

A series of case study projects has been undertaken on what have been referred to as demonstration farms (Countryside Commission, 1984). This work has indicated that there can be a relatively small economic penalty, in terms of lost income, to maintaining an acceptable level of environmental features. It has also been shown that the highly efficient farmers involved and their landlords seem prepared to bear these costs. However, these should not necessarily be regarded as representative of the farming population more widely.

In order to assist farmers wishing to develop conservation values on their farms, the Farming and Wildlife Advisory Group (FWAG) (see for instance Cox *et al.*, 1985 for a discussion) now has full-time advisors in most counties. The policy of FWAG is to act in a purely responsive way; to provide information to farmers seeking advice. While useful, the approach is thus clearly limited and can do little or nothing to counter-balance the pressures for change which continue to result from the CAP and the budgetary pressures to change it.

Clearly, many wish to go beyond this in giving a greater emphasis to conservation values. This implies a need for policy adjustment. But the issue is not necessarily one of farmer against conservationist. Many farmers would be willing, and indeed would prefer, to farm in ways which are more sensitive towards environmental values. But their first concern is to maintain income levels. This suggests that agricultural funding might be redirected to reward conservation efforts rather than agricultural produc-tion, and farm organizations have supported this. Indeed there have been moves in this direction, illustrated by the provision of grants for environ-mental improvements in the 1985 EC Regulation on Farm Structures and the establishment of Environmentally Sensitive Areas.

The greatest pressures on the CAP, though, are budgetary rather than environmental. The prime concern is with means of reducing expenditures. To the extent that the pursuit of environmental objectives can facilitate reduced spending on agriculture, they will be advanced. However, there has until recently been little evidence of a strong desire to pursue environ-mental objectives for their own sake. And there are many competing claims that greater funding should be directed towards other, non-rural areas of Community policy, such as urban redevelopment or regional policy. It is still not clear that any substantial part of the funds which can be clawed back from the agricultural budget will be passed back to farmers for environmental enhancement.

References

Barkham, J. (1989) Trusting the counties. *Ecos*, **10**, 11–20.
Bowers, J.K. and Cheshire, P. (1983) *Agriculture, the Countryside and Land Use: An Economic Critique.* Methuen, London.
Countryside Commission (1984) *Demonstration Farms.* CCP170 Countryside Commission, Cheltenham.
Countryside Commission (1987) *Policies for Enjoying the Countryside.* CCP234, Countryside Commission, Cheltenham.
Cox, G., Lowe, P.D. and Winter, M. (1985) Land use conflict after the Wildlife and Countryside Act 1981: the Role of the Farming and Wildlife Advisory Group. *Journal of Rural Studies*, **1**, 173–83.
Green, B. (1985) *Countryside Conservation*, 2nd edn. George Allen & Unwin, London.
Green, B. (1988) Does the future lie in the past?, paper presented at the initial conference on the *Future Countryside Programme*. Conference Proceedings. Royal Society for the Encouragement of Arts, Manufactures and Commerce, London.
Lowe, D. and Goyder, J. (1983) *Environmental Groups in Politics.* George Allen & Unwin, London.
Lowe, D. and Rudig, W. (1986) Political ecology and the social sciences – the state

of the art. *British Journal of Political Science*, **16**, 513–50.

Munton, R.J.C. (1983) Agriculture and conservation: what room for compromise? In: Warren, A. and Goldsmith, F.B. (eds). *Conservation in Perspective*. John Wiley, London, Chap. 20.

Nature Conservancy Council (1984) *Nature Conservation in Great Britain*. Nature Conservancy Council, Shrewsbury.

Newby, Howard (1985) *Green and Pleasant Land?* 2nd edn, Wildwood House, London.

Newby, Howard (1987) *Country Life: a Social History of Rural England*. Weidenfeld and Nicolson, London.

Newby, H., Bell, C., Saunders, P. and Rose, D. (1977) Farmers' attitudes to conservation. *Countryside Recreation Review*, **2**, 23–30.

Russell, A. (1986) *The Country Parish*. SPCK, London.

Shoard, M. (1980) *The Theft of the Countryside*. Temple Smith, London.

Worth, J. (1984) What we think of the countryside. *Ecos*, **5**, 35–7.

Young, K. (1988) Interim Report: Rural prospects. In: Jowell, R., Witherspoon, S. and Brook, L. (eds) *British Social Attitudes the 5th Report*. Gower, Aldershot, pp. 155–74.

Chapter 6
Land Use by Design?

Ian Hodge

The analysis in Chapter 4 demonstrates clearly the potential for domestic food requirements to be met from a substantially smaller area of land than is now used for farming. What will become of the rest? Is 'surplus' land a problem? The vision of multitudes of bankrupted farmers and vast areas of abandoned land is easily conjured up, but it is not helpful to a more considered analysis of future land use options. It is clear that the future will not be like the past, but it is the perception of the situation, rather than the situation itself which has been through a rapid adjustment in the past few years.

The critical difference for the future which has now become widely accepted is that a major constraint has been removed from the use of rural land. It is no longer necessary to give unfettered commercial agriculture a first claim on the whole area of rural land in order to satisfy domestic pressures for food production. The possible obsolescence of this constraint was foreseen nearly 20 years ago by Edwards and Wibberley (1971). They concluded their discussion of a land use budget with the comment that

> there may be a future in which agriculture will still be using most of Britian's rural land but doing so in a protective rather than an active role with the community choosing to forfeit maximum agricultural output in order to create a rural environment which provides for environmental rather than economic needs.

Why should people regard the situation of 'surplus' land as a problem? There are three main causes of concern. One is that the balance of land uses will fail to reflect the relative demand for the products of those uses. The second is that the pattern of land use will cause avoidable environmental damage or will fail to provide environmental benefits. The third is that the pattern of rural land uses will not generate the desired level of incomes, either for farmers or for those in rural communities who are in some way dependent upon them.

In the past, the support of agricultural prices has been seen as the major mechanism for producing the desired outcomes in response to all of these concerns, but it has failed to secure any of them in the past and it will not do so in the future. In practice separate policies are required to meet each of these objectives. The issue of incomes should thus be treated as a separate issue and is discussed elsewhere. This leaves two major objectives: promoting the appropriate mix of private land uses and securing the public interest in rural land use. While in practice there are overlaps between these areas of concern, the discussion here considers them in turn.

The mix of private uses

Agricultural surpluses

The use to which any particular piece of farm land is put depends to a large extent on relative prices. But the levels of farm prices continue to be set administratively with regard to many objectives and thus do not simply equate to the social value of the farm products. In the absence of price readjustment, it thus becomes necessary to add another tier of policy to adjust for the resultant distortions in market situations. The main problem is that support for agricultural product prices holds too much land in agricultural use and leads to food surpluses.

Apart from milk quotas, the only instrument with which to tackle this problem directly which has made its appearance on the UK policy scene up to now is the arrangement known as set-aside. The Community framework for a set-aside policy was laid down in a Council Regulation of June 1987. This made provision for schemes to encourage the conversion and 'extensification' of production. In the language of the Community, extensification is defined as a reduction in the output of a product by at least 20% without other production capacity being increased. While a set-aside scheme is sometimes argued to cause intensification, it nevertheless fits into the Community definition of extensification.

The set-aside scheme was introduced in 1988 as a mechanism for the reduction of agricultural surpluses. Member countries of the European Community were required to introduce schemes for the 1988/89 season although participation by farmers in the scheme is voluntary. Farmers who enter are required to set aside at least 20% of their land which is growing relevant arable crops. These include most common crops except potatoes and crops grown for stock feed. The land may then be put into permanent or rotational fallow, be transferred to some non-agricultural use (e.g. sport or tourism, but not housing, industrial or retail development) or be afforested. Fallow land must not be grazed except by horses, and it must be kept in good agricultural condition and in a way that protects the environment. As a general rule, the application of fertilizers and pesticides is prohibited. The rates of compensation paid to farmers vary, being between £150 and £200 per hectare outside the Less Favoured Areas and £130 and £180 within them. These amounts are paid annually to farmers who agree to participate in the scheme for five years, though they may opt out after three years, with penalties. Farmers who did not wish to enrol in the scheme immediately could nevertheless register their area provisionally, with a view to possible participation at a later date.

In the first year of the scheme about 1,800 farmers joined the scheme, setting aside nearly 60,000 hectares. Two-thirds of this was in England and nearly 80% of the land was put into permanent fallow. About one-third of the participants chose to set aside their whole farms, but in most cases these represented only small plots, often less than ten hectares. Applications for the second year of the scheme nearly doubled the total area of land to 110,000 hectares.

As outlined, the scheme concentrates primarily on the goal of production restraint. While it offers some opportunities for farmers to enhance nature conservation on their farms, it does not give much incentive to them to do so. In an attempt to meet this criticism of the set-aside scheme, a Countryside Premium, managed by the Countryside Commission, has been introduced in seven counties in eastern England. This scheme, operating from 1989/90, provides extra payments to set-aside participants who undertake positive management of land set-aside as permanent fallow for the benefit of wildlife, the landscape and the local community. The land management options available include the creation of habitat on wooded margins, creation of new areas of grassland to be available for public enjoyment, and the creation or restoration of other habitats.

The extent of take-up and the impact of the Countryside Premium have yet to be assessed. However, some problems still remain. The five-year time period does not offer encouragement for longer-term investments, except in so far as this is to be found in the Forestry Commission's Woodland Grant Scheme (1988) or MAFF's Farm Woodland Scheme (1988). The Council for the Protection of Rural England (1988) criticized the scheme for failing to integrate environmental objectives. In particular, they argued for encouragement to environmentally friendly or low-input farming. There might be more scope for this under the extensification schemes which are currently, in 1989, under consideration. These would require a reduction in farm output without requiring that any specific areas of land should be taken out of production. It would be an objective here that extensification should bring environmental benefit. Schemes are under discussion for beef and sheep and for arable crops.

A further problem of these schemes is that they are also likely to suffer from slippage, in that the net restraint on production would be less than the former production from the area set aside. This would be the case if other land was farmed more intensively than hitherto, or if other land was held in production which might otherwise have been taken out, for instance, land set aside for sporting facilities or horse-keeping would be likely to displace these uses from elsewhere.

Despite such problems and reservations, it seems to have been inevitable that some such form of direct supply control had to be introduced, albeit on a voluntary basis. The goal should be to use such schemes to promote desirable land uses in a cost-effective manner. In the United States, with a long experience of set-aside, conservation has gained an increasing emphasis. Recent thinking there has suggested that set-aside should be targeted on productive land adjoining rivers. This could make a significant contribution to reducing river sedimentation, a major problem in the United States, by preventing eroded soil from reaching water courses, while at the same time guaranteeing a substantial decrease in production. Similar logic applied to the UK would imply that schemes should be targeted on selected areas with a view to the non-agricultural gains to be achieved from reduced production.

Land for development

The logic of agricultural land surpluses has not escaped the developers. In the context of escalating house prices in much of southern England, strong arguments have been made for more land to be developed for housing. But the conversion of farm land for urban development does not depend upon market forces alone. It is strictly controlled by the planning system, so that any expansion depends upon a government decision. In February 1987, in the context of a number of new measures to promote alternative land uses, the Department of the Environment published a draft Circular which proposed to relax the controls over the development of agricultural land. The Circular played down the importance of agricultural considerations in relation to planning decisions so that 'the agricultural implications must be considered together with the environmental and economic aspects'. In particular, it proposed a reduction in the role of the Ministry of Agriculture in considering planning applications, so that it would only have to be consulted where a proposed development involved the loss of 20 hectares or more of grade 1 or 2 agricultural land, compared with the previous limit of 4. Proposed changes of use on grade 3, 4 or 5 land would not normally be opposed on land quality grounds.

The draft Circular produced an immediate political reaction. It was met by a strong criticism from the National Farmers' Union, the Council for the Protection of Rural England and the Royal Town Planning Institute. These forced the Government to retreat on some issues. The final Circular, which was published in May 1987, stresses that the best and most versatile agricultural land has a special importance. It goes on to indicate that where applications relate to such land 'additional weight needs to be given to the agricultural factor' and that 'this does not mean that all other agricultural land is being freed for development'. The requirements for consulting MAFF were also changed so as to include planning applications on grade 3a agricultural land. But, although the circular affirms 'the continuing need to protect the countryside for its own sake,' the principle has been established that 'it no longer makes sense to retain as much land as possible in agricultural use' (DoE and Welsh Office, 1987).

This episode and a similar one over the introduction of a 1984 Circular on Green Belt and Land for Housing (Elson, 1986) demonstrate the solid support which exists for the planning system and for the control of urban development. This support, counteracting the influence of the development lobby, particularly reflects the strong feelings of Conservative back-benchers and Conservative voters in the Tory strongholds of southern England. It suggests that land development may be one area of economic activity which a free-enterprise government will be incapable of liberalizing to any substantial degree. Nevertheless, the situation is not static. Although the debate might have centred around the agricultural requirements for development control, the major concern is really for environmental issues and property values.

The rate at which agricultural land has been taken for development in England and Wales has fallen steadily since the late 1960s. Between 1980 and 1985 the rate was below 5,000 hectares a year, lower than in any other period since the Second World War and even below the rate during the period of the War (DoE and Welsh Office, 1987). At the same time, there is a growing discussion of the possibility of looser forms of urban development. The potential for accommodating new housing more readily into rural areas and for achieving better standards of layout and landscaping has been noted by the Government, who comment that 'it is no longer necessary to insist on packing in new houses at 20 or 30 to the acre' (DoE and Welsh Office, 1987). This points towards a more flexible attitude towards development, with the emphasis on environmental and employment considerations. The irreversible nature of the change in land use, in the context of uncertainty about land requirements in the future, also justifies caution in determining the amount of development permitted.

Where might this development take place? It is not possible to predict in any detail the likely location of new urban development, depending as it does upon a whole range of local factors and planning policies. However, some constraints can be shown at a simplified national scale. These are illustrated for England and Wales in Figure 6.1. This includes the major areas of grades 1 and 2 agricultural land (small pockets of which are not included), and the major environmental designations[1]. Clearly, development over a large area will be restricted on these grounds, but even in the unshaded areas development may be limited by other factors. This suggests that the changed policy is not likely to lead to a free-for-all for developers. Rather, the terms of the debate have been altered and environmental criteria are likely to loom larger in planning decisions.

---

[1] Since this figure was drawn, a second round of environmentally Sensitive Areas has been declared.

Figure 6.1. Pressures on development.

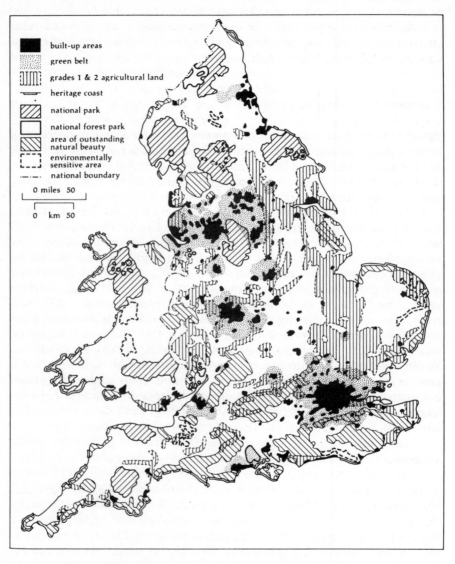

Sources: Countryside Commission; Department of the Environment; Ministry of Agriculture, Fisheries and Food.

Taken from: Owens (1989)

Nevertheless, urban development, even at greatly accelerated rates would make a relatively modest incursion into the area of land which could be released from domestic food supply. If the rate of development was to double from that experienced in the 1980s, it would still take over 600 years to use up the amount of land projected to be no longer required for agriculture by 2015, even with the restricted use of nitrogen.

The wider interest in land use

Besides the issue of the mix of private uses, there is also concern for the wider impacts which land uses have on the rural environment and on access to the countryside. The reduced demand for land for intensive agricultural use generates the potential for reducing the pressures on the rural environment and of providing new areas for nature conservation and access, and of even creating new landscapes. The problem, however, is that farmers face no direct incentive to provide them. While many might be keen to adjust their farming operation in this direction, they are often not in a financial position to do so. The types of changes which conservationists argue for, and which a substantial proportion of the general public appear to support, will not come about in the absence of specific policies.

The need for new policies arises in two forms, which we shall now consider. First, agricultural policies can be amended to promote environmental objectives. Second, specific environmental policies can be designed and introduced. While the latter are in many respects to be preferred, the former are likely to continue to have a more widespread impact. In practice, the distinction between the two categories is not always clear, the difference turning on the extent of the priority accorded to the environmental objectives.

Greening agricultural policies

A variety of changes in agricultural production have led to significant environmental impacts. While agricultural policies are not the sole cause, they have no doubt increased the rate and extent of the changes which have occurred. What scope is there, therefore, for changing policies so as to reverse this process? To the extent that higher product prices tend to stimulate environmental impacts it might be argued that lower prices would reduce them. There is some scope for this, but the effect would be far more complex, including the possibility that new forms of damage might be stimulated. The benefits would arise as a result of a reduced incentive for farmers to intensify; there would be a lower return to land clearance and drainage, a lower return to cultivating marginal soils, and an incentive towards less intensive production. But there would also be other implications. Farmers would tend to shed labour at a faster rate, so that work on environmental maintenance, such as hedging and maintaining stone walls, would be less likely to be done. Also, for some farmers conservation is regarded as something of a luxury. On higher incomes they may be prepared to put land aside for woodland or to use it less intensively. When their incomes fall, they may not be willing to do this. Changes in output prices provide, at best, a blunt instrument for any form of environmental management. In practice, falling prices may in some instances cause more environmental harm than good.

Another possibility might be to influence the size structure of farms towards the type of farm which is most beneficial for the environment. The problem with this is that it is not clear what sort of farm this is. Conventional wisdom generally has it that small farms are good for the environment, and calls for their support are often based on this. But there is no evidence that this is generally the case. Small farms might have a more benign impact to the extent that they are operated in an 'old fashioned' way. But many small farms are not. The other side of the argument less often presented, is that small farmers may be under greater pressure to squeeze a living from their holdings. They may thus be forced to farm their land intensively in order to do this. In practice, neither generalization seems warranted. Most small farmers farm in very much the same way as do their larger counterparts. Equally, some large farms may be owned by commercial organizations and operated by managers with a single financial objective with no room for conservation, but others may be farmed by owners with a strong commitment to conservation and resources to carry it through. Clearly then, policies geared solely towards influencing farm size cannot be relied upon to produce significant environmental gains.

What is required are policies which are more directly aimed at environmental goals. The special measures introduced for locations designated Environmentally Sensitive Areas (ESAs) provide one possible model. These are formulated on the basis of a British proposal which was incorporated into the 1985 Structures Regulation of the European Community. They emerged from a pilot scheme which had been introduced in the Halvergate Marshes and this approach has now been quite widely applied.

The schemes offer payments to farmers who agree to farm in specific ways. For instance, in the Pennine Dales, participating farmers must agree to use less than 20 units of nitrogen, 10 units of phosphate and 10 units of potash per acre per year and not cut grass for hay or silage before a date between the 1st and 15th of July. The specific date varies within the Dales. Farmers are also required to maintain stockproof walls and hedges in a good condition and maintain weatherproof field barns, using traditional materials. In return they receive an annual payment of £100 per hectare. By 1989, 19 ESAs had been designated within the UK in two rounds, in 1987 and 1988 respectively. Ten of these are in England, two in Wales, five in Scotland and two in Northern Ireland. In total, they cover an area of about 8,000 km². The rates of take-up by farmers within ESAs has been high. For instance, by June 1989 in England, the area covered by applications and agreements, about 110,000 hectares, represented over 90% of the land which MAFF had expected to enter the scheme.

Can ESAs offer a prescription for management of the wider countryside? Almost certainly not. They are suitable for areas where specific and easily defined and monitored controls can produce a desired environment. To operate such controls across the whole countryside would be impracticable. It would be difficult to define precise requirements and impossible to monitor them. They would stifle agricultural changes which can improve efficiency and provide no stimulus for the creation of new forms of conservation and landscape.

As has already been indicated, proposals for extensification could concentrate on cutting production by reducing the intensity of agriculture across a wider area. This might be done by limiting the use of chemical sprays or increasing the areas of field boundaries. It would have the advantage of reducing problems of chemical pollution and also have the potential for generating new habitat and conservation interest. Policies could, in principle, simply provide for the long-term cessation of farming within certain areas. However, while some conservationists do favour some land abandonment, in general, landscape quality and conservation interest depends upon human management and for most of the land this will continue to mean some form of agriculture. Simply to suppress agricultural production would not necessarily be good for the environment, unless some other form of management is undertaken.

Other agricultural policies can be and have been designed with environmental objectives: restrictions on grants for productive improvements and new grants for conservation, requirements for participation in set-aside, limits over the use of inputs such as the restrictions on fertilizer use in Nitrate Sensitive Areas. All of these have some potential in particular contexts. But they also have limits. To be applied across a large land area, they must be based on simple, enforceable criteria. They thus can have the role of providing a base line for the wider countryside; for defining the limits of what is generally acceptable. To do more than this requires more detailed evaluation and management. Such policies must have environmental improvement as a central objective.

Policies for the environment

In principle it should be possible to design specialist policies to create the desired effects. But in practice this requires a particular form of investment and management at a specific location. It often requires specialist information concerning the ecology of the area and can require co-ordination between decisions made on neighbouring holdings. Land management in order to produce wider conservation, amenity and access values at this more detailed level is undertaken in two ways: through the use of voluntary management agreements with private owners and by direct management of land by conservation organizations and public sector agencies.

Since the 1981 Wildlife Countryside Act, management agreements have been widely used and much discussed, particularly in order to prevent damage being done to Sites of Special Scientific Interest (SSSIs). As of March 1988, in Great Britain, there were 1,053 management agreements negotiated by the Nature Conservancy Council, in force, covering 38,400 hectares. Payments of about £4.5 million were made to the managers concerned in 1987/88. This type of agreement is also used in National Parks and by local authorities. Similar agreements are also used in order to provide access. These Access agreements were initially provided for in the 1949 National Parks and Access to the Countryside Act and provide financial compensation to landowners who allow public access on their land. It is, however, the use of management agreements on SSSIs which has received most attention.

Management agreements offer a mechanism for a very detailed degree of public control over private land. But inevitably they also require a substantial administrative time and high cost. The detailed requirements need to be carefully monitored and short-term contracts need to be renewed periodically. The system can provide farmers with an incentive to avoid controls by taking pre-emptive action to damage a site prior to designation (Hodge, 1989). The voluntary nature of the agreement leads to long and complex negotiations over the terms to be included. Such agreements, then, offer an important means of protecting valuable sites which remain in private occupation. But they are not necessarily the best way of securing the public interest in rural land more generally.

An ideal arrangement for the management of land can be achieved where the manager of the land values the costs and benefits of land use in exactly the same way as does society more generally (see e.g. Hodge, 1988). The problems facing environmental management arise because some actions cause costs which are valued differently by individual managers and by society as a whole. Some forms of property ownership come closer to the ideal than do others. Where there are no wider social interests in the way in which a particular piece of land is used, then private ownership represents the appropriate arrangement. However, where there are wider concerns, either due to conservation, pollution, landscape or access interests, then other arrangements can be suitable.

In particular, some organizations have the provision of such countryside benefits as a central objective. These include a variety of public interest demand groups. The Royal Society for the Protection of Birds, the Woodland Trust and the National Trust all own and manage substantial areas of land with this wider perspective. The areas owned and managed are shown in Table 6.1. Where the land is kept in agriculture, then the owner will often choose to give up part of the farm income in order to promote the less tangible countryside benefits. Detailed knowledge of the

Table 6.1 Land owned and managed by major conservation bodies in 1988.

	Area (ha)
Royal Society for the Protection of Birds	72,200
Field Studies Council	1,400
Royal Society for Nature Conservation and the Local Nature Conservation Trusts	55,800
Woodland Trust	3,800
Wildfowl Trust	1,900
National Trust[a]	256,000
National Trust for Scotland[b]	39,100

Source: Department of Environment, Digest of Environmental Pollution and Water Statistics, No.11, 1988; National Trust; National Trust for Scotland.
[a] area owned and under covenants.
[b] land owned; alienable and inalienable.

land and control over management, either by managing directly or by making detailed changes to tenancy agreements, gives this type of organization the opportunity and incentive to manage the land in an appropriate way.

The public sector might also fulfil a similar role. Local authority smallholdings may be managed with a variety of objectives (Laxton *et al.*, 1987) which can be far wider than their traditional role of offering opportunities in farming. They can provide access and educational facilities. They can be farmed in order to promote conservation and landscape improvements. New objectives and constraints on smallholdings will also involve lower rents. Thus the local council faces a decision on whether it is prepared to forego rents in order to provide such benefits for the local community.

Institutional land ownership also offers a further advantage in that it breaks the link between land use and individual incomes. For the farmer, low intensity agriculture is largely precluded by his need to make a living. Organizations committed to alternative objectives are not so constrained. They can raise money from other sources: membership fees, donations, entrance fees, rates and so on. They can then manage the land in order to provide new conservation areas, new landscapes, new types of public access, with the demand for their services being reflected in their ability to attract financial support for their activities.

A manifesto on *The Countryside We Want* (Pye-Smith and Hall, 1987) included a proposal for the creation of a Land Bank. The authors suggest that by the end of the century 10% of all agricultural land should be taken out of production. Much of this would become publicly owned and all would be used for non-agricultural purposes: conservation, deciduous forest, recreation and so on. A further 5% would be shifted from private to public ownership but retained for farming. This would be broken up and operated as smallholdings. However, as has been indicated, it is not necessary for the land to be owned by the public sector. The prospects for such an approach in the current political climate does not seem propitious. Public interest demand groups, such as those listed in Table 6.1, can play a similar role and are likely to be more responsive, to the extent that to a considerable degree they depend upon direct payments from the public as a base for their activities. If the past success of such organizations is any guide, they could play a far more substantial role in the future.

Towards a sustainable land use

The notion of 'sustainable development' has become the catch-phrase for those with a concern for the environment. While no one can be against it, exactly what it means is less clear. Pearce *et al.* (1989) list 24 somewhat different definitions. Nevertheless, this concept seems likely to drive the discussion in the next stages of the environmental debate.

At the heart of the concept is a concern that the capacity of our resource base should be preserved for the benefit of future generations. There is fear that a failure to do this will, in the longer term, damage the quality of life, and indeed, ultimately damage the capacity of the planet to sustain human life. This is coupled with an awareness that changes are taking place in the nature of the environmental preferences and in the types of demands which are placed on the environment. Hence there is an emphasis on maintaining flexibility by avoiding irreversible decisions to permit responses to future changes.

Some prescriptions for land use appear to follow clearly and logically from the viewpoint of sustainability: to prevent the irreversible urbanization of agricultural land, to maintain the capacity of the soil by stopping soil erosion, or to avoid the destruction of natural and semi-natural habitats. But such absolute restrictions, though possible, would act as a fundamental brake on economic development, reducing incomes and welfare, both now and in the future. While this fundamental approach might be seen as desirable by some, it seems most unlikely to be a majority view. What is wanted is a more complete recognition of the costs associated with economic development, especially in the longer term, and a reflection of these in current decisions. Beyond this, there is an acceptance of the importance of justice and equity with regard to individual rights and interests, especially of those belonging to future generations. This might well mean that even though certain actions currently appear to be worth-while, taking account of all of the possible foreseeable long-term consequences, they should not be undertaken. For instance, it might be argued that certain spectacular and unique landscapes should not be changed, whatever the possible economic benefits.

But we are still a long way from translating an attitude favouring sustainability into a specific plan for land management. It would be likely to proceed by laying down a set of constraints over land use which should not be violated. For instance, Barbier (1989) has suggested three:

1. Renewable resources should not be used at rates which exceed managed rates of regeneration,
2. Wastes should only be generated at less than or equal to the assimilative capacity of the environment, and
3. Non-renewable resources should not be exploited beyond the rate at which the stock may be substituted by renewable resources or enhanced by technological progress.

Specific prescriptions might follow from these. For instance, that timber should not be felled at a rate above the rate of growth of new timber, or soil should not be allowed to erode at a rate exceeding the natural rate of soil formation. But decisions over other types of land use change are more problematic; even these apparently straightforward prescriptions could be queried. For instance, should a small area of agricultural land be built on and its capacity for food production lost irretrievably for any purpose, or should all land be preserved? Clearly there will be occasions when building on green field sites does take place; and it might be argued that this is permitted by the improved technology which has enhanced the capacity of other areas to produce food (under 3 above). If the concern is with the environmental impact of the building, it might perhaps be argued that some compensating investment in environmental improvement should be undertaken. But decision-making here is very subjective: how can the costs associated with the building on farm land be compared with the benefits of environmental improvement?

The advocacy of sustainable development does not produce clear prescriptions for land use. Rather it represents a different emphasis in decision-making. This emphasis reflects the environmental concerns which are becoming widely held, and for this reason the translation of the principles of sustainability into practical management is an important objective for research. The relaxed constraints over agricultural land represent an opportunity to meet some of these aspirations.

There are plenty of demands for beneficial uses of rural land beyond the conventional ones of unfettered commercial agriculture and forestry: for low intensity farming, for lower density residential use, for recreation, access and landscape improvement. There will also be demands for new agricultural uses. As with any change, it is relatively easy to see what from the past will not be appropriate in the future. It is far more difficult to imagine what will replace it. But this is not to make light of the problems.

There is concern for the mechanisms for meeting the new demands and with the process of adjustment rather than with simply identifying the potential uses. These concerns provide the challenge for the next decades.

References

Barbier, E.B. (1989) *Economics, Natural-Resource Scarcity and Development.* Earthscan Publications Ltd, London.

CPRE (1988) *Comments from the CPRE on the Agriculture Departments' Consultation Document on an Extensification Scheme for Cereals and Beef.* Council for the Protection of Rural England, London.

Department of the Environment and Welsh Office (1987) *Rural Enterprise and Development.* HMSO, London.

Edwards, A.M. and Wibberley, G.P. (1971) *An Agricultural Land Budget for Britain 1965–2000.* Studies in Rural Land Use No. 10. School of Rural Economics and Related Studies, Wye College, University of London.

Elson, M.J. (1986) *Green Belts: Conflict Mediation in the Urban Fringe.* Heinemann, London.

Hodge, I.D. (1988) Property institutions and environmental improvement. *Journal of Agricultural Economics*, **38**, 369–75.

Hodge, I.D. (1989) Compensation for nature conservation. *Environment and Planning A*, **21**, 1027–36.

Laxton, H., Hodge, I.D. and Davidson, J.G. (1987) *Smallholdings Under Pressure: A Review of the Cambridgeshire County Farms Estate*, Occasional Paper No. 18. Department of Land Economy, University of Cambridge.

Owens, Susan (1989) Agricultural land surplus and concern for the countryside, *Development and Planning 1989*, Department of Land Economy, University of Cambridge and Policy Journals, pp. 35–8.

Pearce, D., Markandya, A. and Barbier, E. (1989) *Blueprint for a Green Economy*, Earthscan Publications Ltd, London.

Pye-Smith, C. and Hall, C. (eds) (1987) *The Countryside We Want: A Manifesto for the Year 2000.* Green Books, Bideford.

Chapter 7
The Future Public Pressures on Farming

Ian Hodge

Who and what determines change?

The changing place of farming in the post-war period has been outlined in Chapter 2. As the priorities between alternative policy objectives have altered, together with the capacities of the agricultural sector to meet them, so the approach towards and influences on policy-making have also changed. Immediately after the Second World War, the emphasis was on promoting agricultural production, both because the production was valued in its own right and because it was perceived as simultaneously satisfying other objectives: raising farm incomes, supporting the rural economy and preserving the rural environment. Policy-making was a domestic affair conducted within a relatively small group of like-minded people. This consensus has now evaporated and the process has been complicated and opened out by the UK's entry into the European Community. The production-oriented thrust of agricultural policy is perceived as conflicting with many other objectives, even the agricultural incomes gained are not seen as ending up in the right pockets, and the costs of the policy are generally regarded as excessive. These changes have weakened the productionist thrust of agricultural policy and the technological imperative in change. They have opened up a new range of possibilities.

Farming can be seen as being at the centre of a range of influences and pressures. These influences, such as public opinion, lobby groups, political interests, market forces and technological options, will shape the environment within which farmers will operate. Public opinions influence government policy directly in respect of their implications for votes. But common interests are also expressed through lobby groups which seek to influence the policy process directly as well as through ministries and parliamentary committees. Some lobby groups, such as conservation organizations, depend very much upon broad-based public support and also seek to influence public opinion as a foundation to their aims. Others represent a narrower more concentrated grouping, such as the food industry, and seek to use their influence beyond the public eye. Government policy in turn influences farming in a variety of ways, through investment decisions and constraints on technology, through direct constraints on farming and through its influence on agricultural markets.

All of this has been described in a national context in UK language. This omits the European dimension which has become a central part of the agricultural policy process. The groups of actors in this process are essentially the same even though the administrative structure is different. The policy-making process of the European Community is illustrated in Figure 7.1.

The process of making agricultural policy relating to the United Kingdom now has two clear stages. The influence of the UK actors is thus diluted in the need to find agreement between the 12 member states. But the shift of policy-making towards Brussels has had another consequence. Because of the prominence of agricultural policy within the operation of the European Community and particularly within its budget, agricultural issues are dealt with at the highest political level. This means that agricultural policy has become the standard fare not only of the agriculture ministers, but also of the foreign and finance ministers and, indeed, prime ministers. The summit talks between leaders of the countries of the European Community have for many years tended to be dominated by the issues of milk, cereals, wine and olives.

It must be anticipated that the room for manoeuvre in policy-making at a national level must be further constrained in the future. The signing of the Single European Act in 1987 brings with it fundamental changes in the structure of the Community and in the obligations of Member States. In particular, the Act provides for the establishment, by 1992, of a single market within the Community without internal frontiers in which the free movement of goods, persons, services and capital is ensured. This will require increasing co-operation between national policies.

The state of public opinion

Some aspects of public attitudes towards farming and the countryside in Britain were examined in an earlier section. The results suggest that farmers are generally held in high regard, but that there is a strong element of concern about the countryside and against some forms of intensive production. However, as should now be clear, the future will be influenced not only by British public opinion, but also by public opinion in the other Member States.

Given the differences in agricultural structure and in composition of rural areas between the various countries, it might be anticipated that there would be differences in options about agriculture, agricultural policy and the countryside. Table 7.1 shows the results of a survey conducted by the European Commission in March to May 1987 into the public's views as to the benefits arising from the CAP. This shows that throughout the 12 countries of the EC, only about one-third of respondents believed that

Figure 7.1. The EEC policy-making process. Source: Gardner (1985)

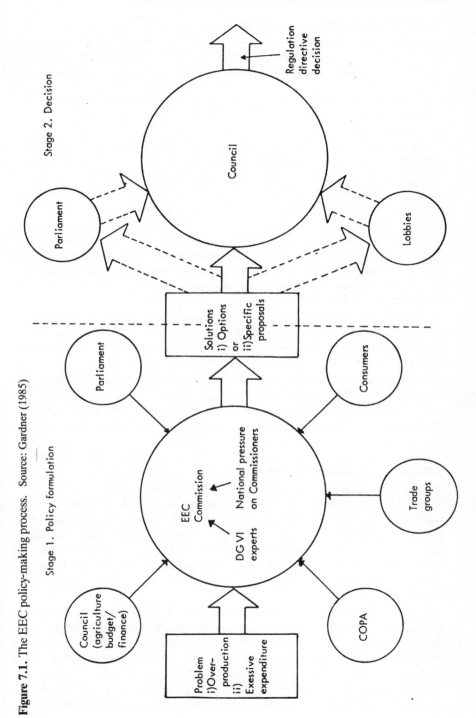

Table 7.1 Public opinion on the benefits from the CAP[a].

	B	DK	D	GR	E	F	IRL	I	L	NL	P	UK	EC12
Farmers have:													
benefited[b]	43	58	30	56	9	38	66	40	47	44	43	34	34
not benefited[b]	23	26	48	25	59	31	10	24	27	34	27	38	37
Consumers have:													
benefited[b]	43	44	51	41	14	40	35	38	41	44	41	28	37
not benefited[b]	25	36	29	34	55	32	39	27	33	32	29	48	36

Source: Commission of European Communities (1987).
[a]based on survey in 1987.
[b]do not sum to 100 due to 'don't knows' and non-responses.

farmers had benefited. In some of the smaller countries, the percentage is higher; in Ireland two-thirds of respondents believed that farmers had benefited. In Spain the figure is dramatically low. If the figures for Spain and Portugal are omitted to allow for the fact that they had only just entered the EC, the figure for the Community of 10 (EC10) rises to 38%, leaving Germany and the UK below the average and the small countries of Belgium, Denmark, Greece, Ireland, Luxembourg and the Netherlands well above it.

Surprisingly, a higher percentage of respondents believed that consumers had benefited. Again, if Spain and Portugal are omitted, the percentage (EC10) rises to 40%. This leaves the UK well below the average at 28%. It is interesting to note that Germany has the highest figure, with over 50% of the population giving a positive response. Two points may be noted from this. First, a lower proportion of the public in the UK believe that either farmers or consumers have benefited from the CAP than is the case in the EC, more generally. Secondly, the prevalence of the belief that consumers have benefited perhaps provides a clue as to the nature of the political support for the CAP in some other countries, notably Germany. While in academic analysis and generally in public debate the benefits are regarded as going to the farmer at the expense of the consumer (and taxpayer), this is apparently not reflected in public opinion. This suggests that political support for the CAP is not just from the farmers themselves.

Table 7.2 shows the results of a survey of farmers, asking the same questions. The proportion believing that they had benefited from the CAP across the 12 countries is similar to the figure for the public as a whole. But there is a wide variation between countries. Denmark, Ireland and the Netherlands produce very high positive responses, whereas Germany and Spain produce particularly low ones. However, because of the higher proportions of definite answers, there is a higher proportion of farmers

Table 7.2 Farmers' opinions on the benefits from the CAP[a].

	B	DK	D	GR	E	F	IRL	I	L	NL	P	UK	EC12
Farmers have:													
benefited[b]	49	81	11	59	7	29	78	37	55	85	41	59	36
not benefited[b]	31	14	81	30	78	57	16	54	37	11	44	33	53
Consumers have:													
benefited[b]	57	76	63	50	17	49	58	49	60	72	41	63	47
not benefited[b]	26	13	29	31	62	34	27	34	27	16	40	28	37

Source: Commission of European Communities (1987).
[a]based on survey in 1987.
[b]do not sum to 100 due to 'don't knows' and non-responses.

who believe that they have not benefited. This represents over half of the entire sample and reaches 81% for Germany. Farmers were also more likely to believe that consumers had benefited than was the general public. It is interesting to note the polarization between the public and the farmers' responses in the UK. Amongst the public, only 28% believed that consumers had benefited from the CAP, while amongst farmers, 63% believed this. There is a much closer convergence of views between farmers and the public in other countries.

There is an obvious danger in trying to read too much into public opinion surveys. But these results do seem to indicate at least one point which might provide some indicators of the public pressures on agricultural policy-making. There is a surprisingly strong belief generally that consumers have benefited from the CAP, although this view is much less prevalent in the UK. This will lend support to politicians who seek to maintain the position of the CAP. The different position in the UK is one element setting British politicians apart from their continental counterparts.

Nutritional concerns and the demand for food

Public opinion exerts a major and direct influence on farming through the demand for food. The volume of food of different types and quality sold in the market depends upon the innumerable choices made by consumers. Changes in those choices must ultimately be reflected in changes in agriculture. Demand generally depends upon prices paid by consumers, incomes, population and tastes. Prices paid by consumers and incomes tend to change rather gradually from year to year and to have little impact on the level of sales from the farm gate. The population is relatively stable and this is likely to continue in the foreseeable future. The greatest potential influence, but also the greatest unknown, relates to consumers' tastes.

Changes in the consumption of some food items over the period 1965 to 1987 are shown in Table 7.3, which illustrates some important and consistent long-term trends. Notable is the decline in consumption of eggs, sugar, butter and bread and the growth in the consumption of cheese. These are long-term trends and not simply responses to the more recent concerns for a healthy diet. Other changes are more recent, such as the increased consumption of wholewheat and wholemeal bread. There are, of course, changes within food groups, which often offset each other. For instance, since 1975 there has been a decline in the consumption of hard, natural cheese and a rise in consumption of soft natural cheese.

Further, attitudes towards health and the use of animals for food could potentially have an important influence on diet. Barfield (1987) has outlined one possible set of changes which could meet the dietary recommendations of the National Advisory Committee on Nutrition Education (NACNE, 1983). Table 7.4 shows the suggested percentage changes from the 1984 level of food consumption as indicated by the National Food Survey.

These figures illustrate the potential changes in quantity and quality of foods consumed. If such a diet was to be widely adopted there would be a major effect on the total requirements of major food stuffs. By way of illustration, a 75% reduction in the consumption of butter, based on the 1984 situation, implies a total fall for the UK of 180,000 tonnes per annum. This compares with total production of butter of 206,000 tonnes,

Table 7.3 Long term changes in consumption of major food items in the UK.

	Ounces per person per week[a]					
	1965	1970	1975	1980	1985	1987
Liquid whole milk (pints)	4.85	4.63	4.76	4.15	3.32	2.88
Cheese	3.20	3.59	3.79	3.89	3.91	4.09
Carcass meat	16.78	15.88	15.30	16.76	13.22	12.59
Fish	5.78	5.35	4.46	4.80	4.90	5.09
Eggs (no.)	4.78	4.66	4.14	3.69	3.15	2.89
Butter	6.10	5.90	5.63	4.05	2.83	2.14
Sugar	17.56	16.94	11.29	11.17	8.41	7.48
Vegetables	88.04	87.55	83.98	85.37	84.93	83.79
White bread, standard loaves	34.31	32.23	27.68	21.87	19.37	16.01
Wholewheat and wholemeal	0.69	0.50	0.69	1.55	3.59	4.73
Total bread	40.60	38.11	33.67	31.12	30.99	30.60

Sources: MAFF (1987); MAFF (1989).
[a]except where otherwise stated.

Table 7.4 National diet amendments to meet NACNE target.

	Quantity percentage change
Liquid milk	0[a]
Cheese	0[b]
Beef, lamb, pork	0[c]
Bacon (liver)	−25[d]
Sausages, meat products	−25[d]
Butter	−75
Margarine	+85[e]
Other fats	−50
Bread	+70
Flour	+25
Cakes, pastry, biscuits	−50
Other cereal products	+50

Source: Taken from Barfield (1987).
Notes: [a]Substitute low fat milk. [b]Reduce fat from cheese. [c]Remove subcutaneous fat. [d]Remove half subcutaneous fat. [e]High in polyunsaturates.

i.e. approaching 95%. This is not to suggest either that this dietary change will necessarily occur in this way or that the reduction would be met from domestic production. But it does highlight the potential scale of change involved. A major shift from livestock products to arable products clearly has important implications for land use. Similarly, a shift towards vegetarianism would lead to the same type of consequences.

There is also much evidence of a change in the concern for the way in which foods are produced. Increasing health consciousness and concern for environment and animal welfare is leading consumers to reject some products. In particular, some consumers have shown that they are willing to pay more for products which are produced in different ways: with lower chemical inputs, without the use of hormones and under improved housing conditions. This is illustrated in the demand for organically produced vegetables and free range eggs. At present, this market represents a small proportion of the total. But it could clearly develop. Food manufacturers and retailers have recognized the power of a healthy image in market promotion and the trend towards product adjustment to meet this demand still has some way to go.

What is less clear is the extent to which it will be pursued. For instance, there are now well-established criteria and recognized logos for organically produced products. These have to meet very strict production standards. However, there is debate as to how far consumers will be prepared to pay higher prices for such high standards. Competing standards are also on offer. A new organization, the British Culinary Institute, has announced a logo for 'natural' British foods. This will be bestowed on those who produce food 'benevolently'. It might perhaps be anticipated that the majority of consumers will not be prepared to pay for the extreme organic standards and that the major food manufacturers will steal the organic producers' thunder by producing intermediate quality products which satisfy the majority of consumers. These might well be met by relatively modest adjustments in agricultural production systems.

There can be little doubt that, more generally, advertisers believe that consumers will respond to a green image. The range of products which has suddenly come to be promoted on the basis of their being in some way better for the environment than their competitors, is remarkable. But the extent to which this represents a long-term and serious shift in consumer preferences has yet to be seen.

What is wanted from the countryside: the conservation interest in land use

It is often stated that conservationists do not make it clear what they want, and although such criticisms have some basis, they are perhaps a little harsh. The countryside could be enhanced in an enormous variety of ways in different places and it is difficult to summarize these in a simple statement. Moreover, there is a range of views among conservationists in their emphasis on the importance of different types of change. One might expect a similar response to questions about the future design of cars. Even with such a well-defined and familiar product, some people would stress safety, some would stress performance and comfort, others would stress fuel efficiency. The range of options and problems of definition are far more acute in respect of conservation.

It is easier to be specific about what most conservationists would like to see reduced: levels of nitrate contamination of groundwaters, rates of pesticide use, pollution from livestock effluent, damage and nuisance from straw burning, and soil erosion. These might be summarized as lowering pollution. But many conservationists clearly would seek to go beyond this, to enhance the wider benefits which are generated from rural land uses, particularly in the forms of nature conservation, landscape quality and public access. Melchett (1985) has outlined his view of what conservationists want:

> Variety and richness of experience; local and regional variation – variety in detail – different wild flowers either side of banks of hedges. The variety that different seasons bring; variety that reflects local historical, cultural, climatic and economic differences. Richness of experience – again variety is a vital ingredient – but the number of animals and birds, flowers and insects, and the availability of opportunities to enjoy all of these is also crucial. Our popular and political support rests

largely on this emotive, spiritual attachment to wildlife and the countryside – *and conservationists must continue to press this.*

Reference has already been made to a manifesto on *The Countryside We Want* published by the 1999 Committee (Pye-Smith and Hall, 1987). This group has produced a set of policies covering the wider social, economic and environmental issues of countryside policy. They propose policies with the aims of providing more work on the land, freer access to the country-side, improved conservation and landscape and a more humane system of animal production. Their policies would promote mixed farming and tenanted holdings. They would reduce price support and phase out produc-tion grants. Instead there would be Land Management Payments for farmers who agree to abide by management, conservation and access agreements. Local councils would play an important role in directly owning land, in a stricter system of planning controls and in making Land Manage-ment Payments. The proposed approach is illustrated by case studies of three areas: North Kent, the Mid-Welsh Hills and Sherwood Forest.

While there might be doubt about the strength and pervasiveness of these types of demands in the population more generally, they have become well-established on the political agenda in the UK. But in the context of European policy-making, what demands are there for environ-mental improvement in the other member countries? One aspect of this which stands out is that the environmental issues and concerns which are debated vary from country to country. For instance, some southern areas of Europe are concerned with forest fires, other mountainous areas are concerned with maintaining forests to reduce risk of avalanches. But even within the northern countries there is variation. For instance, the problem of animal-waste disposal receives more prominence in the Netherlands, while the problem of fertilizer and pesticide pollution has received much attention in Denmark. An action plan set up by the Minister of the Environment in Denmark demands a 50% reduction in pesticide use by the mid-1990s. The extent of the concern for the aesthetic aspects of rural land use appears to be more pronounced in the UK than it is elsewhere.

Despite these variations, opinion polls do suggest a common element of concern for the rural environment across all Member States. This is illustrated by a survey conducted in 1986 (Commission of the European Communities, 1986). One question asked respondents to indicate whether they had reasons to complain about various aspects of their local environ-ment. The majority indicated that they had few complaints. The highest response related to damage done to the landscape, with 32% indicating that they had a 'great deal' or a 'fair amount' of reason for complaint. It is not necessarily the case, however, that the damage was due to agriculture. There was a much higher level of concern for wider environmental issues. For instance, 79% indicated that they had a 'great deal' or a 'fair amount' of concern for industrial waste disposal, 82% were similarly concerned for damage caused to sea life and beaches, and 81% for pollution of rivers and lakes. A high priority is also given to environmental protection. Environmental protection was regarded by 72% of respondents as an urgent immediate problem rather than a problem for the future or as not really being a problem at all.

Once again, it is important to recognize the limitations of this type of opinion survey, but the results do suggest that there is a common concern across the European Community for environmental protection. However, the particular issues of concern vary between countries. This would imply support for a policy which enabled, and perhaps encouraged, restraint on agricultural production in order to promote environmental benefits, but which allowed the detailed questions of implementation to be worked out at a national level.

Electoral influences: agricultural and environmental voting

The agricultural vote

Within a democratic system, for most individuals, the most direct exercise of political influence lies in the casting of votes. But the direct agricultural vote inevitably represents a very small proportion of the total; agricultural employment comprises less than 2.5% of the UK workforce. However, this vote is unevenly distributed across the nation, so that its local influence could be greater. In 1955, there were 110 constituencies in Great Britain where agriculture provided more than 15% of total regular male employment (Self and Storing, 1962). But this figure has declined dramatically under the twin influences of a continuing decline in numbers engaged in agriculture and a growth of the size of the rural population. By 1981, there remained only eight constituencies with 15% or more of employment in agriculture (Johnston et al., 1988). McAllister and Rose (1984) indicate that the most agricultural constituency in England in 1981 was Holland-with-Boston in Lincolnshire, but even there only 18.6% of the workforce was engaged in agriculture.

Rural areas have for a long time been important strongholds for the Conservative Party and it has been shown that the strength of the party's vote has tended to increase with the percentage of the workforce employed in agriculture (Johnston et al., 1988). However, between 1983 and 1987, there was a swing away from the Conservative Party in the rural areas. The reason for this was that these areas showed substantial relative swings to the Alliance. The implications of this for the future are not clear in the context of the collapse in the support for the centre parties.

The significance of voting patterns, however, depends more on the influences of voting changes on the numbers of elected representatives from the respective parties, i.e. it is the marginal constituencies which are of importance. Political parties will tend to adjust their policies so as to influence potential voters in marginal constituencies. In a context of the vote being shared between three or more parties, any analysis of voting behaviour becomes far more complex, and it becomes quite possible that rural constituencies could be seen as important to the success of individual parties. But with a small proportion of the population engaged in farming, it is likely to be the non-agricultural aspects of rural policy which could swing a sufficient number of voters. This will be particularly so where changes favouring farmers are seen as being in conflict with changes favouring other rural voters.

Agricultural interests also depend on the agricultural affiliations of Members of Parliament. In the post-war period, the proportion of MPs with interests in agriculture, as farmers, directors or landowners, has been higher than the proportion in the population as a whole. In the 1983 Parliament, 59 MPs were closely connected with agriculture, representing about 9% of all MPs (Howarth, 1985). However, within Cabinet, there were ten Ministers having close connections with agriculture. The extent of this personal relationship with agriculture among senior policy-makers is often credited as explaining at least some of the influence of agricultural interests on decision-making. But in practice, such influences are difficult, if not impossible, to pin down.

In the other countries of the European Community the agricultural vote is much stronger. In the Community as a whole, over 7% of the workforce is engaged in agriculture. In Ireland, Greece and Portugal, the figure is over 20%. Thus at a regional and local level, the agricultural vote must have a strong influence on political outcomes. Further, under proportional representation and with coalition governments, the voting behaviour of particular interest groups can be critical to the survival of national governments. Even in West Germany, where agriculture comprises only about 5% of the workforce, farm interests have held a strong influence over agricultural policy-making. This has arisen from the coalition politics which have given considerable influence to a relatively small third party in the Bundestag, the Freie Demokratische Partei (FDP). For this party, success in the polls depended upon a few constituencies in Bavaria which were heavily influenced by the farm vote (Hendriks, 1987). This support for agriculture is further reinforced by strong pressures from the churches and a widespread acceptance of the importance of agriculture in the society. But as agricultural employment inevitably declines as a proportion of the total and as the populations in rural areas become more diversified, the direct influence of the agricultural vote must fall.

The environmental vote

If the agricultural vote has been waning, the influence of environmental issues on voting behaviour has shown a dramatic upsurge. Lowe (1988) has discussed the origins of the environmental movement in a European context. Most European countries now have a 'green' party and within the EC, Belgium, Italy, Luxembourg and West Germany have these parties represented in the national parliament. The European Parliament, elected in 1989, contains 29 Greens or near-Greens from West Germany, Holland, France, Italy and Belgium. But other parties too have clamoured to demonstrate their environmental concern in an attempt to steal the ground from the green parties. Thus the consequence of environmental concern is not necessarily to be a widespread rise of specialist environmental parties. Rather, because support for environmental improvement is broadly based, all parties will be inclined to promote green policies.

In Britain, too, environmental issues have become important, but in the absence of proportional representation, the Green Party has been unable to win any seats. There is, though, strong evidence of support. In the elections for the European Parliament, in June 1989, the Green Party achieved a remarkable 15% of the overall vote; some 2.3 million votes.

This should not be interpreted as guaranteeing a central place for the Green Party in British politics; many factors may have influenced the voters' decisions in this particular election. But it does indicate the depth of environmental concern and the extent to which it can influence voter behaviour. Public opinion strongly supports a higher priority for environmental policy. A poll conducted in September 1989 (*Guardian*, 18 Sept 89) found that 70% of respondents believed that the Government should give a higher priority to environmental policy, even if this means higher prices for some goods. And this view was spread very evenly across all party supporters.

The message has not been lost on politicians. Mrs Thatcher showed the way in her conversion to environmental issues. In a speech to the Royal Society in September 1988 she described protection of the environment and the balance of nature as 'one of the great challenges of the late twentieth century'. This conversion is remarkable. Earlier she had been quoted in the *Guardian* as saying 'When you have spent half your political life dealing with humdrum issues like the environment, it is exciting to have a real crisis on your hands.' This sort of turnaround is reflected too in the policy proposals coming forward across a whole range of issues. The extent to which they become implemented in practice has yet to be seen. They will become harder once the costs involved become more fully recognized.

This environmental concern, while it may reject intensive agriculture, should not be regarded as necessarily anti-agricultural. The demand is to promote a particular sort of agriculture and land use. Thus assistance for agriculture will continue to receive widespread and enhanced support, where the type of production encouraged is perceived as being beneficial to the rural environment. But clearly policies which promote greater food output but which threaten the environment will not receive support.

The influence of the lobbies

In exerting their influence on policies, interest groups do not depend solely upon their ability to influence the pattern of voting in parliamentary elections once every four or five years. Predominantly, they use their resources directly to persuade policy-makers, and those close to them, to make particular choices and decisions. As has been seen, the farmers' lobby has been particularly successful in this by becoming incorporated in the policy-making process. Other lobbies are seen as having had less influence. What prospects are there for the lobbies with an interest in agricultural policies in the future?

The farm lobby is led by the National Farmers' Union (NFU), while the particular concerns of ownership are represented by the Country Landowners' Association (CLA). Can the NFU maintain its position of influence over agricultural policy questions? Entry into Europe has inevitably weakened the direct link which the NFU has had with the policy-making process. However, the farm lobby continues to exert its influence in Brussels. The federation of farmers' unions in the European Community, COPA, has the right to be consulted in the CAP decision-making process and wields substantial influence with the agriculture ministers. Gardner (1987) has quoted a senior Commission official as saying: 'the Commission only proposes and the Agriculture Council will only agree what it knows COPA will accept', and comments that this is confirmed by a close examination of the unpublished Commission and Council working group papers. Gardner goes on to argue that the majority of the individuals and the groups involved in agricultural policy-making have as their major objective the maintenance of the *status quo*.

This view is certainly consistent with the past record of the development of the CAP. Whether it continues depends upon the extent to which power can be wrested away from those committed to production. Mrs Thatcher has led numerous assaults on the agricultural position and yet, to date, has rather little to show for it in terms of radical reform. The changes which have been conceded often appear at first sight to place some fundamental limit on budgetary expenditure. But, time after time, in the application, the effects have petered out and been overtaken by further expenditure growth. It is difficult to conceive of a set of constraints which can effectively bind the hands of the agriculture ministers if they remain committed to the agricultural cause. This is not to say that agriculture will not be squeezed by changes in policy. This appears inevitable. But the changes are more likely to be incremental.

Thus the farm lobby has powerful political allies in Europe, but many issues remain to be resolved on a domestic basis and here the position of the NFU is perhaps under greater threat. The ability of the NFU to maintain its leading position depends on a variety of factors. In a context of production growth and confidence in the agricultural industry, it is relatively easy for farmers to act together. The relative gains of one group of farmers over another may be tolerated in an expectation that the position for all can be improved. But under pressures of constraint this communal feeling may be less easy to maintain. The NFU tends to be dominated by large farmers, whose situation strongly influences the political perception of the UK's bargaining position in CAP negotiations, given the relatively large farm size structure of UK agriculture. However, in the context of surpluses, the logical direction for an agricultural support policy under budgetary restraint must be towards targeting support on small and low income farmers. It should be no surprise if small farmers in the UK feel that they have closer allies on the Continent than they do in Agriculture House.

Other interests appear to have less influence on policy-making, especially at the European level. Both consumer groups and the food industry make representations in seeking to influence the development of the CAP. However, the impact of the food industry is difficult to assess since its lobbying activities are much less open than those of the farm interests. While consumer groups represent a large number of people, their interests are diverse and they have failed to gain the close relationship with the policy-making process which has been achieved by COPA (Senior Nello, 1989).

A more recent influence over rural policy comes from the environmental movement. The environmental lobby has clearly come of age in the mid-1980s and has increasingly concerned itself with questions of agricultural policy, with strong support from the media. Some environmental groups, such as Friends of the Earth, have come to command considerable attention in their own right. Other, often more narrowly focused groups coordinate their efforts under two umbrella bodies, Wildlife Link which lobbies the Nature Conservancy Council (NCC) and Countryside Link, which lobbies the Countryside Commission. As has been noted earlier, the grassroot support for environmental interests has given this lobby a new strength. But its ability to influence developments has been limited by its distance from the relevant centres of power. While the Ministry of Agriculture (MAFF) has a Cabinet Minister to represent its interests, which must in large part reflect those of the farmers themselves, the two conservation agencies (the NCC and Countryside Commission) have no such direct link. They are represented through the Department of the Environment, which is concerned with a vast array of other issues. The struggle between the two lobbies is thus to some extent played out in the form of a contest for influence between two government ministries in areas where their interests overlap.

The direct influence of the environmental movement on the development of the CAP is much less apparent. In her discussion of European interest groups and the CAP, Senior Nello (1989) does not even mention environmental interests. Given the widespread concern for environmental issues within the Community, this is perhaps surprising. However, as is the case with consumer interests, the institutional arrangements of CAP decision-making make access for such groups difficult. It seems more likely that they can exert greater pressure at a national level via the Council of Ministers.

The pressures on farmers

It is many years since farmers were left to get on with things in their own way in a free market. But the state intervention in the past has been primarily concerned to enable them to do more of what they wanted to do: produce food. The intervention will persist, but the direction in which public pressures are pushing may not be the direction in which most individual farmers want to go. Some, of course, will seize the opportunities which will inevitably be available; to meet the demands of a health-conscious population or to satisfy the demands for leisure activities. For many, the effects on their day-to-day lives will be gradual and in many respects will not amount to much more than a continuation of the pressures they have experienced in the past.

References

Barfield, A. (1987) Diet advice and the demand for food, paper presented at the Agricultural Economics Society Annual Conference, Reading.
Commission of the European Communities (1986) *The Europeans and their Environment in 1986.* Commission of the European Communities, Brussels.
Commission of the European Communities (1987) *Eurobarometer* No. 27. European Commission, Brussels.
Gardner, B. (1985) The political realities. In: *Perspectives for the Common Agricultural Policy*, Agra Europe Special Report No. 28, Agra Europe Ltd, London.
Gardner, B. (1987) The Common Agricultural Policy; The political obstacle to reform. *Political Quarterly*, **58**, 167–79.
Hendriks, G. (1987) The politics of food: The case of F.R. Germany. *Food Policy*, **12**, 35–45.
Howarth, R.W. (1985) *Farming for Farmers?* Institute of Economic Affairs, London.
Johnston, R.J., Pattie, C.J. and Allsopp, J.G. (1988) *A Nation Dividing? The Electoral Map of Great Britain 1979–1987.* Longman, London.
Lowe, P. (1988) Environmental concern and rural conservation politics. In: Whitby, M. and Ollerenshaw, J. (eds), *Land-Use and the European Environment.* Belhaven Press, London, pp. 68–77.
MAFF (1987) *Household Food Consumption and Expenditure 1985.* HMSO, London.
MAFF (1989) *Household Food Consumption and Expenditure, 1987.* HMSO, London.
McAllister, I. and Rose, R. (1984) *The Nationwide Competition for Votes.* Frances

Pinter, London and Dover.

Melchett, P. (1985) A conservationist's observations. In: Baldock, D. and Conder, D. (eds), *Can the CAP fit the Environment?* CPRE/IEEP, London, pp. 75–6.

National Advisory Committee on Nutrition Education (1983) *Proposals for Nutritional Guidelines for Health Education in Britain.* Health Education Council, London.

Pye-Smith, C. and Hall, C. (1987) *The Countryside We Want: A Manifesto for the Year 2000.* Green Books, Bideford.

Self, P. and Storing, H.J. (1962) *The State and the Farmer.* George Allen & Unwin, London.

Senior Nello, S. (1989) European interest groups and the CAP. *Food Policy,* **14**, 101–6.

Chapter 8
Incomes and Wealth

Berkeley Hill

Introduction

Incomes in agriculture are central to many of the changes seen in the British farming industry during the period covered by this book. In a dynamic world farmers find that they have to be continually on the look-out for new income-generating opportunities, not just in order to grow (as any successful businessman will endeavour to do) but also to protect their incomes against the steady erosion arising from the basic economics of farming.

An appreciation of incomes and their determination is fundamental to the explanation of the disappearance of the small farm and the concentration of land into a decreasing number of ever-larger holdings; to the inevitable spread of new technology and the tendency of farmers to press for higher production; to increasing specialization; to the land prices that farmers face; to the rising level of part-time farming; and to many other changes which so often have repercussions which stretch beyond farmers to society at large. Incomes also help explain why the number of hired agricultural workers has fallen and continues to shrink as existing staff seek better opportunities in other jobs and as potential new entrants are deterred from entering this industry.

Concern with incomes is also a principal reason why the UK government has maintained an agricultural policy, a concern that it shares not only with the governments of the other members of the European Community (and puts into practice through the CAP) but with governments of virtually all industrialized countries.

The study of incomes in agriculture generally concentrates on the incomes of farmers and their families, an approach taken here. This is justified on the grounds that many of the developments in the agricultural industry are related primarily to farmers' incomes and, within agricultural policy, support is directed almost exclusively at them. But hired workers are also part of the agricultural industry and arguably present more of an income problem than do farmers. However, the factors determining their incomes are different; the hired labour force is given separate consideration in a later section.

Factor incomes and personal incomes

Incomes can be looked at in a variety of ways, and it is necessary to distinguish these in order to avoid the confusion that so often clouds their discussion. First, income can be regarded as the reward to factors of production for taking part in an economic activity, such as farming. This represents the reward to the owners of factors for generating the output of goods (livestock and livestock products and crops), most of which are sold to other parts of the economy. Farmers have an income which is the reward to a mix of inputs they own – capital, land, their labour, and management input. In a similar way, farm workers sell their labour to help in production in exchange for a wage, and landlords sell the services of their land for rent. The rewards from agricultural activity can be viewed at the level of the individual farm business or of the entire industry.

Second, income can be viewed as the amounts that people in a particular occupation group, such as farmers or hired workers, receive from all sources – their total personal incomes. The personal incomes of farmers may be obtained predominantly from their farm businesses, but will cover other income sources as well. Because households, or at least husbands and spouses, tend to share their income and expenditure, it is a common practice when assessing personal income to take the household as the unit rather than the individual. It is also customary to make use of the concept at the level of all farming households taken together – the entire agricultural household sector of the economy.

In a world where farm families owned all their land and capital, worked only on the farm and had no other form of earned or unearned income, the two approaches of 'income from agricultural activity' and 'total personal income' would coincide. However, the existence of a growing body of part-time farming households and the presence of income from other property (such as interest received), pensions and other sources means that it is necessary to keep in mind the question: is it income from agricultural production or some form of personal income that is appropriate for consideration in particular situations? So often the former has been used where the latter is implicitly in mind. This leads to misunderstanding, to false comparisons and to wrong conclusions, as will be made evident later. Both approaches can be considered at the levels of the whole industry (all farmers taken together) or of the individual farm business or family.

The income of the agricultural industry

Since the Second World War the *Annual Review of Agriculture* (renamed in 1989 as *Agriculture in the United Kingdom*) prepared for Parliament by the Agriculture Departments, has contained calculations of the aggregate income of the industry. This is one element in the Agricultural Accounts, drawn up as if the industry were one national farm. Though from time to time there have been changes in the methods used in the calculations of the industry income, understandable but inconvenient to the observer of long-term trends, the basics have remained unaltered. From estimates of the value of all that is produced on the national farm (its gross output) deductions are made for the inputs purchased from other industries (fertilizer, fuel and so on), for rents paid, for costs of hired labour and interest, and for depreciation of capital items, leaving an income figure (called Farming Income in its latest manifestation). This is the residue remaining to reward the farmer and his spouse for their physical and managerial input and for the capital and land they own. Other aggregate indicators are now presented alongside the Farming Income figures (Farm Business Income, Cash Flow, and Net Product) but it is Farming Income which has the longest history and commands the greatest attention. This has been widely interpreted as a ready-made indicator of the prosperity of farming, but it should be noted once again that it is not the same as the total income of farmers and their families; still less does it represent the amount that agricultural households can spend on maintaining their living standards. (See, for example, HMSO (1989) for recent estimates and MAFF (1984) for an historical series. For a description of the national agricultural accounting system see Outlaw and Croft (1981) and for the available official series on incomes see Lund and Watson (1981).)

To understand what has been happening to the income position of the farming industry, and to make assessments of the likely patterns for the next decade, the vital distinction between the quantity of output that farming generates and the value of that output must first be studied. Any attempt to assess the future prospects for farming or the welfare of farm people must begin with the recognition that these two measurements do not move in step with one another. This, more than any other single factor, has been the root cause of farmers' material disappointments, sense of insecurity and financial distress.

It is well known that the amount produced by UK agriculture (in physical terms of tonnes and litres) has risen substantially in the last three decades. This is shown in Figure 8.1; the volume of gross output in the mid-1980s was about double that of the early 1950s. Apart from dips caused by poor weather conditions in occasional years, notably in the mid-1970s, the trend has been inexorably upwards, at least until 1984. However, mainly because the prices which farmers receive for their products have been declining in real terms (that is, once inflation has been taken into account) the value of agriculture's gross output has not been rising. It is clear from Figure 8.1, that the real value of output increased hardly at all in the 1950s and 1960s despite the rapid growth in the volume of production. The early 1970s saw a sudden jump in value, corresponding with the entry of the UK to the EC and the gradual adoption of its system

Figure 8.1. Volume and value of UK agricultural output. —+—, gross output, volume (output at constant prices); □, gross output, value (current prices deflated by the RPI).

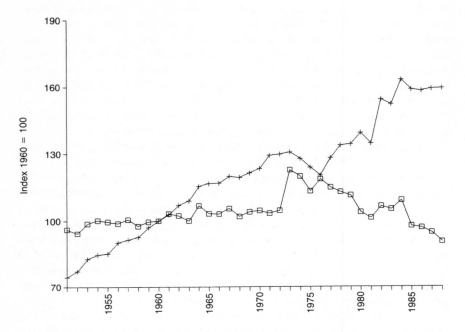

of support which initially brought higher product prices, and with an international boom in the prices of agricultural commodities which had an impact within the UK. However, since that time the value of agricultural output has suffered a sustained decline in real terms, so that the total in 1988 was little different from that of 1951, despite the impressive increase in quantities delivered from farms and a consequent saving in food imports.

This failure of the value of farming's output to expand, and indeed its downward movement since 1973, is not really surprising in a country like the UK. With a population well fed and steady in size, spending a declining proportion of its income on the basic food material as its prosperity expands from year to year, the demand for additional agricultural output is small. Self-sufficiency has risen to the extent that there are few remaining opportunities to substitute home-production for imports. On the supply side, technological advances taking place partly within agriculture but more especially in its supplying industries (the plant breeders, the chemical and machinery manufacturers and so on) have been taken up and spread throughout farming with the inevitability of a treadmill. Most of these advances have the result of generating more production from farms. Consequently, rising output faced with a static demand is bound to result in oversupplied markets and to declining prices for farm products. This is the market mechanism working to signal that less output is required, and is an inevitable outcome of the circumstances in which British agriculture finds itself. Moreover, it is common to advanced economies in general. All the efforts of the CAP to support prices have not been sufficient to withstand the fundamental economic forces, which now threaten to engulf the Community's whole budgetary structure.

In line with what has gone on in recent decades, the next 20 years are likely to witness a further downward drift in the real value of agricultural output. If attempts to constrain expansion of production are successful, the decline will be more muted. This may indeed be achieved in some sectors, but it is unlikely that the effect will be sufficient to counter the tendency for the treadmill of technical advance to push up production and to push down real prices for agricultural production as a whole. Only a substantial transfer of productive resources out of agriculture, or an unexpected emergence of new and assailable markets at home or abroad, will prevent a further deterioration in real prices – and deprive consumers of ever cheaper food in the years to come.

The changing value of output is only half the story when describing the income situation of British agriculture, though it is perhaps the most crucial since it is the more volatile side. The other half is the cost of all the resources which farming uses; income is the difference between the two. Figure 8.2 shows the way in which the various groups of inputs absorb the revenue from output; the total height of the columns corresponds to the value of gross output (after correcting for inflation). The main costs are stacked on top of each other, with the residue – the top section of the column – as income. The way that each cost item has varied over time is more readily seen when plotted individually (Figure 8.3). Once again this is illustrated after taking into account the influence of inflation and is thus expressed in 'real' terms.

Where, then, has the money flowing into the farming industry gone? The largest share of expenditure goes on items purchased from other industrial sectors – fuel and machinery parts, chemicals in the form of fertilizers and disease and pest control, purchased livestock feed, the services of accountants and other professions to name just a few. The value of these inputs jumped in the early 1970s, mirroring what was happening to output, but since then, and contrary to popular belief, the value of these purchased inputs has been falling, once inflation has been taken into account. The downward trend in their total cost seems fairly well established and likely to continue, but not at a fast enough rate to prevent a further squeeze on income. However, the decline in this total real cost has not been as large as the downward movement in the value of output, so there has still been a tightening squeeze on the margin between the two, and this is unlikely to be relaxed by market forces.

But there are also the other costs which farming has to face – interest charges, rents on tenanted land, the cost of employing labour, and the

Figure 8.2. Value of gross output in real terms: total and composition.

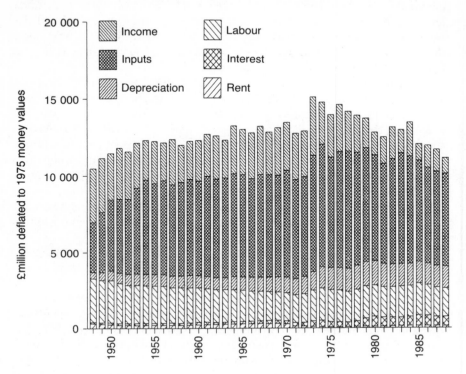

depreciation charge which should be deducted to allow for the wearing out of machinery, buildings and other capital assets. Their relative importance can be seen in Figures 8.2 and 8.3. Of these, the smallest item is rent for tenanted land; the drop in the rent series at 1970 represents a change in the method of calculation rather than a real movement in rents. The cost of labour declined in real terms in the 1950s and 1960s but since the early 1970s has been remarkably constant; rising wage levels have been offset by fewer employees. Interest charges saw a rise in the 1970s but in the 1980s have increased little. Depreciation gradually increased up to 1980 but since then has started to fall, following the pattern of investment. While these items play some part in the explanation of the income position of the industry, it is the value of output and the cost of inputs purchased from other industries that tend to dominate the situation.

A characteristic of the agricultural industry is the short-term variation in its income situation, a feature which may serve to disguise the longer-term decline. This inherent instability is due to the impact of influences on output which are beyond the control of farmers – principally the weather. The value of inputs in total varies less from year to year than does gross

Figure 8.3. Separate components of value of gross output, in real terms. +, rent; □, interest; ×, labour; ▽, depreciation; #, inputs; ◇, income.

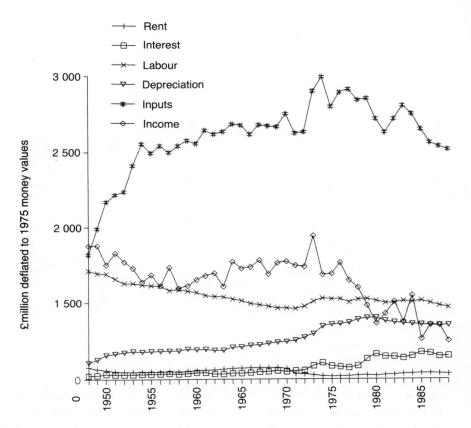

output. This implies that farming income, the 'cream' left over in the agricultural accounts, varies by a greater proportion than does output value.

There is another long-term tendency which has aggravated the instability of the income from farming, namely the increased proportion of purchased inputs to total output. This arises as systems of production become more intensive and new technology substitutes bought-in inputs for those generated within agriculture itself (energy from diesel fuel in place of horses, inorganic fertilizers in place of or in addition to manure, and so on). In other words, the share of gross output which is left for farmers has been declining; this is more easily seen in Figure 8.4, where farming income falls from over 30% of gross output in the 1940s to less than 20% in the 1980s. When fluctuations on the value of output are superimposed on this narrowing margin, the implication for greater income instability is self-evident.

Figure 8.4. Farming income as a percentage of gross output.

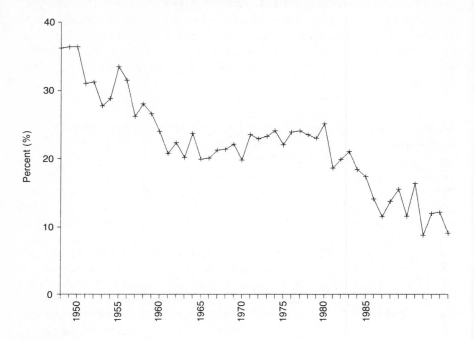

Reward by function

Sometimes commentators on the agricultural scene have been concerned with the share of the rewards that are taken by the owners of land, the owners of capital and the labour force and, consequently, how much is left to compensate farmers for their efforts in the industry. There is a general desire to make comparison between the rewards available for human enterprise in agriculture and in other sectors of the economy, and to do this free from the complicating factors of rent and interest. The way that the national agricultural accounts are presented does not allow this reward by function to be demonstrated. Interest as currently shown relates only to borrowed capital, not to that owned by the farmer and his spouse. Furthermore, the interest covers only borrowing for commercial farming purposes and excludes that on loans for land purchase, a somewhat arbitrary division in practice but supported on theoretical grounds in the UK because it is felt that landownership is an activity separate from farming, a distinction not accepted in the rest of the EC and at variance with the accepted Community aggregate accounting system. Similarly, rent is only for tenanted land, not all land. The labour cost figures include the reward to all hired and family labour, though not the labour input of the farmer and spouse. These excluded items are embraced within farming income which thus contains the reward to a bundle of factors of production – owned capital, owned land, the farmer and spouse labour and management inputs. Thus the UK accounts are partly a breakdown by function and partly by ownership. A thorough analysis to determine the return to each factor separately would require substantial assumptions on the levels of charge to be made for owned factors and would be open to challenge on both theoretical and practical grounds.

Income indicators used in the EC: the influence of numbers of people

While an abstract view of the total income generated by the agricultural industry is possible, for purposes of government or EC policy it has to be related to the numbers of people among whom the income is shared. The fact that the aggregate income may be declining is tempered if it is known that there are fewer people sharing it, and the per capita farming income may even be rising while the industry income is falling. Within the EC the usual practice is to express income measures averaged over the number of individuals involved in its generation, expressed as annual work units which brings all workers, both hired and the self-employed parts of the labour force, to full-time equivalents. This seems to reflect an interpretation of the Common Agricultural Policy's objectives as being aimed at the benefit of all people involved in the industry; this is in contrast with the position in the UK where the assumption tends to be that the CAP operates for the support of farmers rather than for the benefit of the total agricultural workforce (including the hired workers).

Three levels of indicator are used (Eurostat, 1987):

Indicator 1. Net Value Added at factor cost per Annual Work Unit
Indicator 2. net income from agricultural activity of the total labour input per Annual Work Unit ('labour income')
Indicator 3. net income from agricultural activity of the family labour input per Annual Work Unit of family labour ('farming income per family labour unit')

The way these indicators relate to each other is given in Figure 8.5. In the terminology used in the UK agricultural accounts Indicator 3 approximates to farming income divided by the number of farmers and spouses expressed in full-time equivalents. Indicator 2 is equivalent to the reward available for all people engaged in farming (both in the form of wages of the hired sector and profits of the self-employed farmers after meeting all direct costs) averaged over the complete agricultural labour force. In countries where the number of hired workers is small and where their incomes are similar to those of farmers this combined income figure may be acceptable, but for the UK it is probably more satisfactory to avoid the

Figure 8.5. EC indicators of agricultural income.

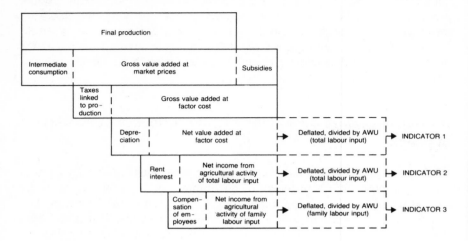

pooling of these two groups and to concentrate on Indicator 3 which is concerned only with the income of the self-employed sector.

Figure 8.6 shows the change in each Indicator for the period 1973–88, with the average of the years 1979–81 treated as 100. As with the earlier presentations, this figure shows 'real' incomes after taking inflation into account. The main point emerging is that, even when the falling number of farmers and spouses are allowed for, there has been a substantial fall in the average income from farming per family labour unit (Indicator 3) in the UK since the early 1970s. On the basis of past trends – and there is little to suggest that any new major factor has arrived to upset the general drift – this measure of income is not likely to show any significant rise in the immediate future. If hired labour is also included (whose numbers have been falling far more sharply than those of farmers) then the decline becomes far more muted, with little deterioration since the late 1970s. However, as was pointed out above, Indicator 2 is of limited applicability within the context of the UK.

When looking forward and trying to trace the likely development of UK agriculture over the next couple of decades, basing projections on the national Agricultural Accounts and those from the EC, it seems inevitable that the downward movement in the industry's income will continue in real terms, or at the very best stay at about the present level. Of course this assumes that the present forces continue to operate with the existing balance and ignores the possible implications of large-scale nuclear disasters, of a new oligopoly arising in the oil market, of large-scale war or other major disturbances to the world economy. In the absence of these, the fundamental economic pressures at work will continue to constrain the income of the agricultural branch of the economy; as has been pointed out

Figure 8.6. Farm indicators for the UK, +, Indicator 1; □, Indicator 2; ×, Indicator 3 (see text).

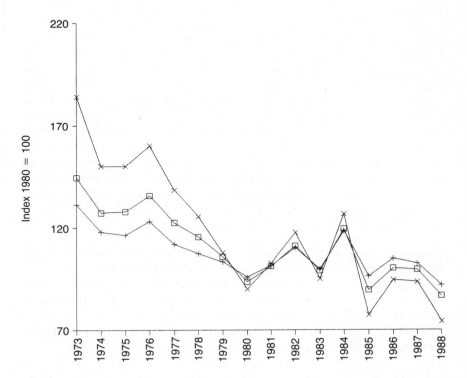

earlier, this is simply the underlying market forces at work (either directly or as a constraint on the amount of support supplied by governments) adjusting the use of resources in line with the changing pattern of demand and the advance of technology.

Incomes of individual farm businesses

Estimates of the income of the entire agricultural industry obscure the fact that the income situation on a farm of a particular type or size may bear little or no resemblance to what is happening at the national level. Even within one category, say dairy farms of medium size, there will be substantial variation brought about by particular circumstances of weather, management and other factors, including luck. The diversity of income patterns can only be demonstrated using microeconomic data, and this generally means from surveys.

The annual Farm Business Survey in the UK (finance by central government but largely carried out by universities) is the major source of information. Its prime purpose is to gather information on short-term changes in the prosperity of farming, and it uses accounting conventions appropriate to this end. Unfortunately the nature of the sample and some of its methodology means that it is not possible to gross up the survey results to national levels and make direct comparisons with the aggregate accounts for agriculture; if this were feasible the UK would have an extremely rich and powerful set of data with which to monitor its farming industry. Although there have been recent changes in its methodology (MAFF, 1988), the main income indicator (Net Farm Income) treats all farms as if they were tenanted, imputing a rental value for owner-occupied land, evidently for the reason that this enables farms of different tenures to be put on the same cost basis and their accounts to be grouped. For similar but more complex reasons, interest charges, for whatever purpose, are ignored in the survey. Thus Net Farm Income is of only limited value in assessing anything other than changes in the prosperity of farming from one year to the next arising from price or cost movements and changes in productivity. The annual reports primarily use group averages to describe the developments of income, though individual business data are also drawn upon. Despite the drawbacks, average Net Farm Incomes of groups of farms can be used to indicate broad developments in agriculture as long as the conventions used are borne in mind. Because the survey deals with businesses and expresses results as a per-business average, the gradual growth of farm size is captured in the results.

In broad terms the main findings on income from the Farm Business Survey are:

1. That different farming types (dairy, livestock, cropping and so on) show widely different income trends in the medium and short term.
2. That small farms generally have lower incomes than larger ones of the same type, though the wide variability means that some small ones will have bigger incomes than some larger farms.
3. That the variability from year to year within farming types has become more exaggerated in the 1970s and 1980s compared with relative stability in the 1950s and 1960s.
4. That year-to-year variations tend to be greater among small farms than among larger ones.

The recent introduction of income indicators (Operators' Net Income and Farmers' Flow of Funds) which reflect to a greater extent the real situation faced by farmers (for example, by treating land tenure as it actually is and deducting interest charges) should enable further trends to be identified, though it is too early for these to have emerged. (These were introduced in the 1987 edition of MAFF's *Farm Incomes in the United Kingdom*. The 1988 edition contained estimates of Occupier's Net Income for a reduced sample of farms in England and Wales for 1982/3 to 1986/7, the longest period for which such information is available.)

Though the general direction of movement in income per farm in the various farming types is undeniably downwards, in line with the macro-economic indicators, there are considerable short-term departures from the trend. It is also worth noting that the large rise in aggregate income seen at the beginning of the 1970s was duly reflected in the farm accounts monitored by the Farm Business Survey and the increase in yearly fluctuations also stem from this time.

Apart from the increased variability since 1970, the other characteristics noted above have been long-standing features of this farm accounts survey. Thus there is little reason to expect any change in the next two decades or so, though the degrees by which they are manifest could well alter. Thus we can expect the smaller farm still to be characterized by smaller and more variable incomes, a combination which will ensure the continued decline in their numbers. The disparate way in which weather affects different types of farming is equally sure to continue, and while some effects will be widespread (such as the droughts of 1975 and 1976) others will endow special good or bad fortune. These will tend to mask the underlying long-term trends. The greater income variability since the early 1970s could have a variety of explanations, including the shrinking margin between revenues and costs already mentioned and the way in which the agricultural support system has switched to one based more on the market. The upshot is that this higher degree of year-to-year change is unlikely to moderate unless there is a change in the way that commodity regimes operate towards ensuring a greater degree of product price stability – not a strong possibility in the present budgetary situation of the Community and having regard to the general antipathy of most Member States to the deficiency payment system which had a strong stabilizing influence on UK farm incomes in the 1960s.

There is one other microeconomic source which can be investigated to throw more light on to incomes from farming – the Structure Survey carried out as part of the requirements of the European Community and, in the UK, operated in conjunction with the Agricultural Census. This does not collect information on actual incomes, but the physical data enable estimates of gross margin (revenue less variable costs – approximating to gross value added at market prices) to be made for each holding using standards derived from other surveys and calculations. These standard gross margins (SGMs) form the basis of the size classification used both in the EC (European Size Units) and the UK (British Size Units) since they reflect the amount of farming activity taking place better than a simple measure of land area. In the absence of any direct measure of income, SGMs can be used to suggest how much of the total is accounted for by farms of different sizes and to changes in these proportions.

The estimates show a very skewed distribution. The 12% largest holdings in the UK (40 British Size Units and over) accounted for over half the total SGM in 1988 (56%) whereas the smallest holdings (of less than 4

ESU) represented 44% of holding numbers but only generated 3% of the total SGM. While the distribution of incomes would not exactly reflect these for SGMs, the two are sufficiently linked to suggest a wide disparity of incomes within the farming industry, confirming indications to this effect already given by the Farm Business Survey which covers some 3,800 farm businesses each year. Another feature of this form of analysis is that the degree of concentration of SGMs into the hands of the largest producers has been increasing, suggesting that large farm businesses now account for a bigger share of the total income than they have done in the past. Unless there are positive attempts to limit this trend, such as by placing limits on the size of farm or the introduction of measures to encourage more small-holdings, neither of which seem likely in the present climate, the disparity of income will continue and perhaps even become more extreme.

The personal incomes of farmers

So far comment has been restricted to the incomes generated by farm businesses or, earlier, to that coming from the whole agricultural industry. However, in assessing the income position of farmers as people (as opposed to operators of agricultural production units) the measures described above fail to cater for the fact that many have some income in addition to that coming from the farm. It has been demonstrated in Chapter 9 that on a substantial minority of holdings (about one-third) the farmer and/or spouse has another 'gainful activity', in practice implying another job either as an employee or in self-employment. Typically the other activity of the farmer is another business or profession run in parallel with the farm. Evidence from the UK and other industrialized countries points to a continuing growth in the proportion of part-time farmers. In addition to these incomes there are many other sources, some contributing only small amounts, which should be considered when arriving at a total income position; these include pensions, interest and dividends received, family allowance and other welfare transfers. Together they make up total personal income. In this context it is more appropriate to look at the farmer and spouse as a unit and to treat their incomes in common, as normally both income and expenditure are shared. A case could also be made for taking a broader view and looking at the complete household's income; this is considered later. In order to estimate the amount that the household has available to spend on the costs of living, deductions can be made from personal income (for taxation and other obligatory payments) to leave a measure of disposable income.

   In the UK it has not been customary to study the total personal income of farmers as part of the annual assessment of the state of the industry. As was pointed out at the start of this chapter, the traditional macroeconomic approach is to measure the income generated by the branch of the economy labelled agriculture, designated by the type of commodities it produces. At farm level the Farm Business Survey has largely confined itself to measuring the income generated by the farm business, ignoring any non-farming income which the farmer or his spouse may have. In the next 20 years this is all likely to change, with estimates of personal income being made and put alongside the existing indicators, though not replacing them. At aggregate level there will be much more interest in the total income of that part of the population who are farmers – a sector approach – and at farm level data will be collected on all sources of income accruing to the farmer's household. Preparations are already being made in official circles for these new income indicators. In 1987 the Statistical Office of the European Communities has announced its intention to publish information on the total disposable income of farmer households in Member States (probably from the early 1990s). In the UK figures from the Inland Revenue showing estimates of farmers' total taxable incomes were presented for the first time in the 1989 White Paper *Agriculture in the United Kingdom*, though they were not fully comparable with the accounts for the industry and were recognized as exploratory at this stage.

These changes are being brought about partly because of a growing appreciation of the complexity of the income sources of modern farmers and partly through a desire to make policy more efficient by targeting support more specifically on those in greatest need. The aims of agricultural policy are dealt with in Chapter 10 but it is worth repeating that, of the various strands which can be identified, the one of ensuring a fair standard of living for the agricultural community (referred to in the second part of Article 39 of the Treaty of Rome) has become the most important. The assortment of policy measures which together make up the CAP are now primarily directed at the income objective. If the main purpose was to balance supply and demand in the market and incomes did not have to be considered, many of the mechanisms could be demolished and the problem of surpluses would go with them.

What is considered a 'fair' standard of living has never been precisely spelled out by the CAP, as neither was the 'proper remuneration and living conditions' mentioned in the 1947 Agriculture Act which guided UK policy up to entry to the EC and which is still the framework for national policy. However, it is clear that living standards are related more to the total income position of farm households than just to the business income generated by their farms. A system of income support which operates through raising the prices of farm products is patently inefficient in that it helps the large output farmer (who is likely already to have a very adequate standard of living, judged by the norms of society) more than the small output farmer who may face a genuine low-income problem. It also will help the farmer with a substantial off-farm income whose total income may be very satisfactory, though his farming income may be low. Indeed, such a farmer may keep his farming income purposely low in order to avoid high marginal rates of taxation. Any revision of agricultural policy to make it more efficient at combating low living standards, and at the same time avoiding surplus production and containing the total costs of policy, will need to have greater information on the total income of farmers than is currently available in the UK.

There are a number of apparently simple decisions to be made before progress in this direction can be made, decisions that are much more complex on further examination and which will shape the future nature of agricultural policy in the UK. First among these is the necessity of deciding who is a farmer and therefore entitled to benefit from agricultural support. Living on a farm, or even being the owner of a farming business, is not a very satisfactory indication. For example, there are many industrial barons who are, nominally, owner-occupier farmers; are they intended beneficiaries of support from the rest of society on income grounds? And what about the elderly person who has land but relies primarily on pensions for his livelihood? Or the lady operator who spends all her working time on her smallholding but who is married to a prosperous solicitor? Several possible criteria exist, but a plausible definition of a farmer would seem to require that farming should be the main income source of the operator and spouse.

This criterion, already used by some EC states, would cut out many of the part-time farming couples and those with substantial investment incomes. It would also mean that some operators of large farm businesses would also be excluded if they had other major interests; however, when considering other agricultural parameters, such as the total value of output, it would be improper to leave them out. This raises an important point; a definition of farmer must be chosen which is appropriate to the issue under consideration, something that also applies to the choice of income measurement.

Another definitional problem arises in deciding whose incomes should be added together for purposes of assessing personal incomes. While there would be little objection to summing those of the farmer and spouse and any dependent children, the position is less clear when other adults form part of the household (farming brothers, elderly parents, grown-up children with off-farm jobs). Households have a variety of arrangements for sharing costs, but simple pooling of incomes is not usual, so summing does not give a realistic picture of the total income available to the individual who might be regarded as the head of the household. Problems of this sort have not yet been resolved to the point where official statistics of agricultural household incomes have emerged, although the fact that satisfactory positions have been reached in a number of other EC countries (and in Britain for the Household Budget Survey) suggests that in due course the UK too will overcome the difficulties.

Not only does this personal income approach allow an assessment of the total income of agricultural households to be made in terms of distributions or in respect to an arbitrary yardstick, such as the income level below which Family Income Supplement might be payable, but it also allows a start to be made in the comparison of the income situation of farmers and non-farmers, for long an aim of administrators of the CAP.

Before turning to the information on total incomes of farmers in the UK it is worth reviewing some common patterns found in countries where data have been available for some time (US, Canada, Germany, Denmark, France, Ireland). Similar patterns might be expected here. These show that farm families have been receiving an increasing proportion of their total income from non-farm sources; in the US for example since 1966 the non-farm income of farm operators has been greater than their farm income and in the first four years of the 1980s non-farm income exceeded income from farming by over 50%. Second, non-farm income tends to be more stable from year-to-year, damping the volatile nature of farming income and imparting a degree of stability to total income. Third, many of the farms which have low farming incomes, including losses, are shown to have total incomes which are far higher as a result of other income sources, greatly reducing the numbers of households for whom some assistance from public funds might be needed; farm income is no reliable guide to the relative total income position of the farmer's household. Fourth, relatively low total incomes tend to be found not on the smallest farms (which typically have substantial non-farm incomes) but among those which are just large enough to be operated full-time by the farmer (and his immediate family) – the small farm on the margin of commercial viability.

At present the only large-scale source of information on the total income of UK farmers comes from the Survey of Personal Incomes (SPI), based on Income Tax returns. For technical reasons the findings cannot be compared directly with the aggregate accounts for agriculture or with the results of the Farm Business Survey; there are differences in income conventions, in timings and in coverage. Methodological developments are likely in the next decade in these areas which will permit the integration of these information sources. However the SPI, even in its present state, suggests some important insights.

Couples and individuals are classed as farmers on the basis of evidence of some self-employment income from agriculture. The sample therefore includes full-time and part-time farmers, though some with very minor amounts of agricultural income may not be covered. Farmers who arrange their businesses as companies and who are (technically) employees of their own companies rather than self-employed are not covered. These tend to be the larger farms and represent a significant gap in the statistics; high farming incomes are probably understated. (For a precise description of the coverage see MAFF (1988).) Husbands and spouses are treated together and their incomes summed.

For all farmers together in the UK defined in this way in the tax years 1977–78 to 1986–87 self-employment income represented between 51 and

64% of total taxable income. Not all, but most, of this would have come from agriculture. Working for others (that is, as employees) constituted 14–20%, pensions 4–6% and investment income 18–23% of total taxable income. This clearly establishes the need to take into account the non-farm sources of income when assessing the total income levels of British farmers. When groups with different levels of total income were examined for a single tax year (1984–85), it was seen that in no group was income from self-employment more than two-thirds of total income, with the lowest contribution from this source occurring in the bands with the smallest incomes and the largest incomes. Employment earnings and investment earnings were proportionally greater at each end of the income spectrum but pensions were most important among low-income farmers and declined in relative importance as higher income bands were reached.

Comparison of the taxable incomes of farmers with other groups in society on the basis of taxable income is strewn with methodological problems. However, one attempt (Hill, 1984) for the late 1970s found that farmers represented a higher proportion of cases as the level of income rose; in the range £1,000–£8,000 they formed only 1% of cases but this increased progressively to 7% in the band £20,000 and over. This is not the sort of characteristic that would be expected if low incomes were a general feature of the farming community.

Though information on total income is not plentiful in the UK, policy developments are going in the direction which dictates that more data are going to be required from farmers on their incomes from non-farming sources if they are to continue to benefit from public spending under the CAP. To some extent this is already built into the qualifications for some capital grant schemes (in which more than half the income has to be from the holding). The proposals for more direct income payments, pre-pensions and other measures envisaged in the 1985 Perspectives Green Paper from the Commission and introduced in a reduced form since then, also require such information. This must be seen as the precursor to a more general situation in which the incomes of the agricultural population have to be presented in a more transparent way than hitherto, something that, in the UK at least, will not be welcome by a large section of farmers.

Wealth of farmers

Information on the wealth of UK farmers is, if anything, even less readily available than that on personal incomes. Policies aimed at incomes are incomplete if they take no notice of wealth. Yet this is very much what has happened in UK agricultural policy since the Second World War. Though there is now a greater attempt to look at the balance sheet of farming at the same time as incomes are considered, this does not constitute the radical revision which now seems justified.

The reasons why wealth in agriculture must be treated at the same time as income can be summarized thus. First, real estate (land and buildings) forms a high proportion of the value of the total assets used by owner-occupier farmers; about two-thirds of the farmed area in Great Britain is owner-occupied. Second, increased levels of support for agriculture are soon translated into higher land prices, so that the ultimate benefit comes not so much as higher incomes but rather as greater wealth. In this situation landowning farmers and landlords have in the past benefited from appreciating land values in a way that tenant farmers could not. History has shown a long period of capital gains arising from increases in land prices, though there has been a recent downturn. Third, capital gains are a form of income which may be turned into current spending power in several ways, most significantly by borrowing against higher asset values; many owner-occupiers have weathered financial storms by extending their borrowing in this way. Fourth, capital gains have been taxed more lightly than current income – often escaping tax altogether – and there is no wealth tax in the UK. Therefore there has been an incentive for farmers to arrange their businesses so that potentially taxable income has been converted into wealth; the main way this has been done has been by buying extra land, and the tax regime has encouraged this by allowing the interest on loans for land purchase to be offset against income. For much of the 1950s to 1970s this tax concession, coupled with high inflation, gave farmers a negative real rate of interest on loans, generating a strong motive to buy land on credit. Fifth, the combination of a link between agricultural product prices and land values, a marginal land market dominated (in the vacant possession sector) by farmers wishing to expand to gain both immediate tax advantages and longer-term capital gains, has produced a situation where, particularly on small farms, low incomes were often found associated with high wealth. The adage that farmers live poor but die rich has been more than hearsay for several decades.

As with income, information on the capital position of agriculture as a sector of the economy is available, but very little on the personal wealth of farmers. Official estimates of the balance sheet of agriculture are available only from 1970 onwards. For earlier decades the problem lies with poor information on liabilities. For a longer-term view it is necessary to resort to land prices expressed in real terms; this is not too much of a disadvantage since the balance sheet is dominated by real estate – typically between 70 and 80% in the last two decades. Real land prices approximately doubled between the late 1950s and the late 1960s, and the consensus is that agriculture enjoyed substantial capital gains. Since 1970 both the assets and liabilities of agriculture (covering all items) have been estimated, so net worths can be shown. This decade and a half has witnessed both a massive rise in net worth and a subsequent reversal, so that the general level in 1986 was similar to 1970, though shared between rather fewer farmers (Figure 8.7). It is clear that the pattern in net worth has followed closely

Figure 8.7. Assets, liabilities and net worth of UK agriculture. +, land and buildings; □, total assets; ×, total liabilities; ▽, net worth.

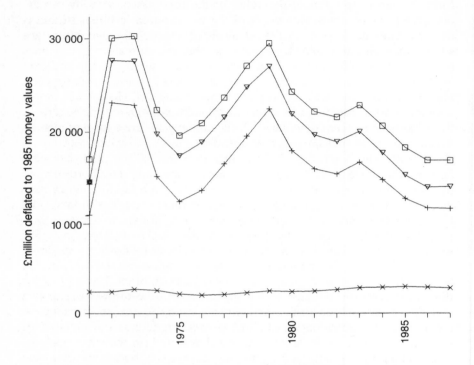

that of real estate. Liabilities have risen in real terms in the last decade, but the main determinant of net worth has been the valuation put on the land. Twin peaks in the early and late 1970s have been followed by a decline in net worth in the 1980s.

Liabilities are by no means evenly spread throughout the industry; a small minority of farmers, typically those who have bought land recently, account for the bulk of the borrowings. In 1969 over half the farm businesses in England had no liabilities, other than short-term credit implied by not settling trade bills until the end of the accounting period. Although the level of indebtedness has probably increased since then, variability is still evident. In the mid-1980s the Farm Business Survey found that in its (non-random) sample half the farms were lightly indebted, with liabilities of less than a quarter of total assets, and on only 13% of farms did liabilities amount to more than their non-land assets (MAFF, 1987). Falling land prices will obviously affect the net worths of the small group of heavily indebted ones disproportionately. Tenant farmers are in a substantially different situation from owner-occupiers with regards to their net worths, at least from those who inherited or purchased before the 1970s.

How the capital position of farm businesses translates to the wealth of farmers and their families is uncertain, though there is likely to be a close association because farming is an activity which is almost completely operated and owned by families (as opposed to public companies). Establishing the personal wealth position of farming population would need information on their non-farming assets and debts, of which almost nothing is known, certainly not enough to chart net worths over a number of years.

The lack of published data on personal wealth means that we must be content with anecdotal evidence and generalities. First, landowning farmers tend to be found in the wealthiest sector of society (Peters, 1980). In the late 1970s even the small dairy farms (occupying one or two men full-time) represented net worth that put their owners among the richest 6% of the population, and occupiers of most sizes and types of farm were in the top 2% or less. Second, agricultural wealth tends to be more evenly distributed among the farming community than is wealth in general among the whole of society. Third, inheritance is a characteristic of the way that agricultural wealth is acquired (Harbury and McMahon, 1973). Fourth, a variety of legal devices (mainly Trusts) are frequently used to ensure the continuation of family control of blocks of agricultural wealth, to which must be added the cushioning against capital taxation that is provided in legislation (Commission, 1981). These characteristics are not likely to alter in the next few decades. However, there may be a greater attention given to the wealth of farmers when assessing their suitability as candidates for support from public funds; a more rigorous scrutiny of the way that the CAP operates will not pass over the paradox that income support represents a transfer from consumers and taxpayers who are, in general, less wealthy than the farmers who are benefiting.

Incomes of the hired labour force

Hired workers have usually been neglected in discussions of agricultural incomes in the UK. Policy aimed at income support has generally had in mind the incomes of farmers and their families, with hired workers treated as outside the immediate sphere of interest and subject to another set of determining factors and government mechanisms. This conscious separation, which is not evident in most other European countries, seems at least partly due to the relatively large size of the hired element in the UK compared with the rest of the EC which has put it in a special position (hired non-family workers contributed 37% of the UK's total agricultural labour in 1983 compared with 11% for the EC as a whole). The existence of the Agricultural Wages Board and the annual survey of incomes and conditions of farmworkers has served to isolate this group from mainstream policy. However, the designers and administrators of the CAP take a different view. Their statements on the interpretation of policy and the measures of income which they use reflect a concern with the incomes of all the labour engaged in agriculture, both the self-employed and the hired sectors. Consequently the disparity which is evident in the UK between the incomes of farmers and of hired workers sits uncomfortably within the CAP.

Most discussion centres on the earnings of the male worker, and how it compares with the incomes of other groups of industrial worker. Though the official monitoring system covers a range of types of worker, no regular series are published on the total income of the households of agricultural workers. While the opportunities for employees to take additional jobs must be limited in view of the number of hours worked in farm employment, the earnings of spouses and other family members are likely to be very significant in terms of household resources.

It is not difficult to demonstrate that hired agricultural workers are among the lowest income earners in society. According to the Low Pay Unit, agricultural workers came fourth from bottom in the nation's wage league and in 1982 38% of its adult male workers were below the official poverty line, taken to be the threshold for Supplementary Benefit entitlement (Winyard, 1982). It must be remembered that this category of hired worker is a fairly narrow one; in 1986 there were 134,000 hired full-time male workers (of which 32,000 were members of the farmers' families) out of a total hired force of 219,000 (excluding seasonal and casual labour). The rates of pay and incomes of other groups of employees (part-time, girls, male youths) may differ considerably. For the purpose of estimating total earnings (a main function of the annual labour inquiry), payments in kind are valued at nominal rates. However, the extent to which perquisites offset low pay has, according to some, been grossly exaggerated (Winyard, 1982); bearing this in mind, workers in tied cottages were found to be about £2.20 better off in weekly earnings than others in agriculture (Philpott and Tyler, 1986).

In terms of relative rates of pay (which will be different from household income) farm workers in 1960 received 65% of manual industrial earnings, a drop from the position in 1949 of 69%. After 1972 earnings in agriculture rose faster than in other industries and by 1976 they had reached 72% of non-agricultural earnings, since when the relative position has remained at about this level (MAFF *Agricultural Labour in England and Wales* (annually)).

The reasons why farm workers are paid so relatively poorly are complex, and it seems unlikely that these influences will change to their advantage over the next few decades. The Agricultural Wages Board, by establishing a legal minimum wage, puts a floor in the labour market, but this is widely interpreted by farmers as the effective basic rate. Agricultural workers are typically in a weak market situation, unless there are particular skills involved or unless the local demand for labour is unusually strong because of some non-agricultural influence. In an economy which has a pool of urban unemployment, the opportunity for many farm workers to transfer to unskilled or semi-skilled jobs in local industries, where these exist, is limited.

In its present employment agricultural labour cannot do much about its wage levels for a number of reasons. These include the scattered nature of the work-force, the smallness of work groups, the problem of organizing effective industrial action and, particularly, the fact that many farm workers have a personal relationship with their employers, frequently finding themselves working alongside the farmer. While this closeness may permit the easy negotiation of minor supplementary payments above the legal minimum wages, it militates against action for a more radical improvement.

Whereas the economic and structural factors which contribute to low incomes are unlikely to become more favourable, the drift to a more technical environment is probably set to continue. Agriculture now shares with mining the unenviable distinction of being at the top of the industrial risks ladder. The last few decades have exposed the farm worker to greater levels of mechanization and more chemicals, and fewer but larger machines have tended to bring more isolation. A combination of these factors, together with housing problems, difficult social conditions and the low wages, will continue to make employment on farms an unattractive proposition for most who are not already there and an insufficient reward to retain many of the more able when family responsibilities reduce the earning power of the worker and his spouse.

Incomes over the next decades

There are some unmistakable and well-established trends in the income situation of agriculture and of the people who take part in it. They stem largely from the persistent way in which the increase in the supply of agricultural products exceeds any expansion in market demand. These trends will continue, though they may be overlaid by events which are incapable of precise prediction and which serve to divert attention from them. Any extrapolation of the past to the year 2000 and beyond has to acknowledge that a major military conflict could transform the income position of UK agriculture, as happened at the time of the Second World War. So could a nuclear accident, or natural disaster so far unimagined. Here we assume that no such major disturbances occur.

Many trends have been mentioned in this chapter, and it is worth bringing the major ones together as a conclusion to this consideration of incomes in agriculture. With an eye to the year 2000 and beyond, the likely changes are these:

1. Though the volume of agricultural output in the UK will continue to expand, the value of gross output in real terms will continue the fall which started in the early 1970s.

2. The income remaining to the owners of farming assets (owned land, owned capital and own labour) will continue to shrink as a proportion of the value of output.

3. Farming income, as calculated in the national Agricultural Accounts, will continue to decline in real terms, though perhaps not quite as fast as has been experienced since the mid-1970s.

4. These changes will be mirrored at the individual farm business level, though with considerable variation between farming types, sizes and tenures. Much will depend on the speed with which the number of separate farms falls. However, it is inevitable that the smallest businesses on which the operator relies exclusively for his livelihood will be increasingly unable to generate an acceptable income. The minimum viable size of a full-time farm will continue to rise. Some farmers will attempt to diversify into non-agricultural activities on their farms, but the successful ones are not likely to be those under the greatest financial pressure but rather the able entrepreneurs who identify new business opportunities.

5. The proportion of farms that are run by households where there are other forms of earned income will rise, especially among those who treat the farm as only a minor source of their livelihoods. As the result of this, and as farming incomes decline, the proportion of the total income coming to farm households from non-agricultural sources will rise.

6. An increased awareness of the size and composition of the total personal income of farmers will force a re-assessment of who are considered farmers and a revision of policy towards those who are in need. Those who gain most of their incomes from other sources will not be classed as farmers. Government support will take a more direct approach to those whose total personal incomes are unsatisfactorily low. Consequently, support for other types of farm operators – those with substantial incomes either because their farm businesses are of adequate size or because of other incomes – will be reduced. This will be brought about principally through lowering prices for farm products, a solution in accord with achieving a better balance between supply and demand. The speed with which such a revision of policy takes place cannot be entirely within the control of the UK, as a common stance has to be shared by Member States within the EC.

7. The wealth of farmers will drift downwards as land prices continue to decline in real terms. However, this is not likely to cause widespread financial stress as farmers adjust to expectations of long-term decline in farming profits and the period of high and, in retrospect temporary, land prices of the 1970s is left behind. Strong demand from wealthy non-farmers for farmhouses and farms for domestic purposes will help support prices overall, being felt particularly among the sales of small areas.

8. The income position of the hired labour force is not likely to improve significantly. The factors which keep its wages low are not likely to alter much, and only a much stronger demand in local labour markets could be expected to raise income levels.

The extent to which most of these changes occur will be dependent on the amount of resources that the government and the EC are prepared to use to support farming incomes. There is a danger that short spurts of policy activity produce effects which are misinterpreted as reversals of the long-term trend. Set-asides and quotas may modify the income position of the groups of farmers to whom they apply, but in terms of countering the fundamental economic forces which dictate changes in resource allocation they are only palliatives. We can expect that wealth patterns will come to reflect new forms of property rights, such as the rights-to-produce (e.g. milk quotas) and payments not to exploit land with special environmental characteristics for farming purposes. However, wealth of this sort, dependent on policy mechanisms, is particularly sensitive to changes in legislation brought about by swings in political opinion.

Until very recently it could have been confidently expected that, with public intervention so important to the size and shape of the agricultural industry, governments would be sensitive to pressures to maintain support to incomes in agriculture. This seems no longer the case, at least as far as the UK Conservative government is concerned. There is an enhanced awareness that incomes in agriculture perform dual roles – those of allocating productive resources and of providing a means of achieving a standard of living. In the past, support aimed essentially at the latter has resulted in a distortion of product and input markets which ultimately has proved unacceptably costly in terms of budgetary expenditure and political sustainability. While there may be good reasons for supporting personal incomes of farmers in some areas for social or environmental ends, a general case for support of incomes seems no longer accepted. For the generality of agriculture, a greater exposure to competitive market forces seems to be the future. Where personal incomes are to be supported, this need not be done through the farming process; alternatives which are more in the nature of direct income payments, or incentives to carry out environmentally desired improvements, may be more effective.

The ability of policy in the UK to move in this direction is constrained by membership of the EC, although within the CAP there are signs that this decoupling of the production and social aspects of agricultural support has taken hold. Perhaps the lesson has been learned that attempts to counter fundamental economic forces, in which incomes play a key part and of which the CAP forms the largest-scale example to date, are destined to be ultimately unsuccessful.

References

Commission of the EC (1981) *Factors influencing the ownership, tenancy, mobility and use of farmland in the United Kingdom*. Information on Agriculture No. 74 Luxembourg: the Commission.

Eurostat (1987) *Agricultural income: sectoral income index analysis 1986* Theme 5, Series D Brussels-Luxembourg: EEC.

Harbury, C.D. and McMahon, P.C. (1973) Inheritance and characteristics of top wealth leavers in Britain. *Economic Journal*, **83**, 810–33.

Hill, B. (1984) Information on farmers' incomes: data from Inland Revenue sources. *Journal of Agricultural Economics*, **35**, 39–50.

HMSO (1988) *Annual Review of Agriculture*. Cmnd 67, HMSO, London.

HMSO (1989) *Agriculture in the United Kingdom 1988*. HMSO, London.

Lund, P.J. and Watson, J.M. (1981) Agricultural incomes: a review of the data and recent trends. *Economic Trends*, **338**, 103–21.

MAFF (1984) *Departmental Net Income Calculation: Historical Series 1937/8 to 1974/5* Statistics Division 1. MAFF, London.

MAFF (1988) *Farm Incomes in the United Kingdom: 1988 Edition*. HMSO, London.

Outlaw, J.E. and Croft, G. (1981) Recent developments in the economic accounts for agriculture. *Economic Trends*, **335**, 95–103.

Peters, G.H. (1980) Some thoughts on capital taxation. *Journal of Agricultural Economics*, **31**, 381–396.

Philpott, J.C. and Tyler, G.J. (1986) *An analysis of the distribution of agricultural workers' earnings in England and Wales*. Report Series No. 17 Oxford University: Institute of Agricultural Economics.

Winyard, S. (1982) *Cold Comfort Farm: a study of farm workers and low pay*. Low Pay Unit, London.

Chapter 9
Part-time Farming and Pluriactivity

Ruth Gasson

Definitions and extent of part-time farming

Although it is customary to treat British agriculture as a separate and in many ways unique sector of the economy, using its own, non-transferable resources, served by its own Ministry and government departments, experiencing a set of problems dissimilar to those of other industries, the justification for continuing this special treatment may be brought into question. Especially is this true of the farm population, since nowadays many farmers and members of their families are simultaneously employed in agriculture and in other sectors of the economy.

According to the 1985 EC Farm Structure Survey, 21% of UK farmers pursued some other gainful activity (OGA) in addition to doing farm work at home. This figure is quite low compared with many of the world's developed countries. The Structure Survey indicated that 31% of farmers in the European Community had other paid jobs, the highest levels being found in Germany and Greece. The phenomenon is more widespread in the United States and Canada than in Britain. Very high levels are recorded in Japan, where seven out of eight agricultural holdings are farmed in conjunction with other jobs (Arkleton Trust, 1985; Robson, 1987).

This combination of farming with other employment is variously described as 'multiple job holding', 'rural pluriactivity' and 'part-time farming'. None of these terms is ideal; the first two are clumsy and the third tends to be confused with working less than full-time on the farm or with operating a farm requiring less than one whole-time worker, situations which do not necessarily coincide. Here 'part-time farming', the most familiar term, is used to denote the combination of farming with other paid work.

Most farms are run as family concerns. In most cases it is the farm family or household rather than the individual farmer whose income needs have to be satisfied and whose labour is available to be deployed, on or off the farm, to meet those needs. For this reason it makes sense to define part-time farming in terms of the farm household rather than the individual farmer or farm. Ideally all farm household members who work and contribute to a joint household budget should be included in the definition. Because of the difficulties of collecting income data, it is more realistic to confine attention to farm occupiers and their spouses. Part-time farming, then, involves a couple combining farm work with other gainful employment. The Labour Input Inquiry, part of the 1983 Structure Survey, used a definition along these lines, although the spouse's OGA was only recognized if she or he also worked on the holding. On the basis of a sample survey, the Labour Input Enquiry found that just under a third of main holdings in the UK were operated on a part-time basis in 1983. Had it been possible to include also 'minor' holdings, cases where household members other than the farmer or spouse had other paid jobs or where one spouse worked exclusively on and one exclusively off the farm, the figure would almost certainly have been higher.

On a conservative estimate, therefore, one-third of farm households in Britain in 1983 had a second source of earned income. In many cases the second source was the main one. From a survey carried out by Wye College in 1984 of a representative sample of the 52,000 main agricultural holdings in England and Wales which reported an OGA for farmer or spouse in the Labour Input Inquiry (Gasson, 1988), it was estimated that two-thirds of part-time farming couples had earned half or more of their income from non-farm or off-farm activities in 1983. The discovery that at least one-third of families living on main agricultural holdings in Britain are not wholly dependent on farming for their livelihood and one-fifth not even mainly dependent, has important implications for farm household incomes, for farm structure and performance and for the rural population.

Implications for farm household incomes

In the first place, most part-time farming families enjoy adequate incomes when earnings from all sources are taken into account. From the Wye College survey it was evident that earnings from other sources often exceeded farm incomes by a wide margin. An estimated 8% of households with OGAs had farm incomes of £10,000 or more in 1983/4 whereas 36% had earned £10,000 or more from other activities. Some 38% of part-time farming households reported making a loss or only breaking even on their farming enterprise in the latest financial year, whereas only 7% reported no net income from the other activity. Taking all income sources together, the majority of part-time farming households appeared to be in a sound financial position; low farm incomes were balanced by high earnings from OGAs and vice versa.

Table 9.1 estimates the level of earnings of all part-time farming households in England and Wales in 1983 on the basis of income information disclosed by respondents in the Wye College survey. It suggests that some 42% of households had made less than £2,000 from farming in the

Table 9.1 Distribution of part-time farming households in England and Wales by level of farm and other earnings in 1983/4.

Farm income £000s	Earnings from other sources in £000s				Total
	Under 2.0	2.0<5.0	5.0<10.0	10.0 and over	
	(% of OGA holdings where income disclosed)				
Loss/nil	5.6	6.7	9.0	17.0	38.3
Under 2.0	4.7	4.4	7.3	8.3	24.7
2.0<5.0	5.3	5.1	3.2	7.3	20.9
5.0 and over	5.7	4.1	2.2	4.1	16.1
Total	21.3	20.3	21.7	36.7	100.0

Source: Wye College survey.

latest financial year but had earnings of at least £5,000 from other sources. (At that time £5,000 was roughly the average UK wage.) Some 17% of households were in the more extreme position of earning at least £10,000 from other sources while making a loss or only breaking even in farming; this would include some who for tax reasons were anxious to show a loss on the farm account. At the other extreme, 6% of households had earned more than £5,000 from farming but less than £2,000 from OGAs in the latest financial year.

Fewer than 10% of the 52,000 OGA households were believed to have made less than an average worker's wage in 1983/4. Some of these households had pensions or unearned sources of income, some had had an exceptionally bad year on the farm and some may have deliberately under-reported farm income. After taking all these factors into account, only a small number of part-time farming families were thought to have unacceptably low levels of income. For the rest, the 'problem' of low farm incomes is no longer a problem. A policy of supporting farm prices in order to maintain the incomes of farm families would appear to be inappropriate in such cases.

Implications for farm structure

Farmers who do not rely wholly on farming for a living may be less responsive to signals from the market than full-time farmers. This could be seen as a weakness in that resources in agriculture will be slow to adjust to changing economic pressures. Taking a broader view, part-time farming may be seen in a more positive light. Freed from the need to increase output in the face of falling returns in order to maintain his income, the part-time farmer is less likely than the full-timer to add to the production of unwanted surpluses. He is less likely to be trapped on the 'technological treadmill' and consequently to pursue farming practices harmful to the environment.

Part-time farming is concentrated on holdings which make only a small contribution to aggregate farm production. Table 9.2, based on the 1983 Labour Input Inquiry in England and Wales, shows that 40% of holdings reporting an OGA for farmer or spouse were below 4 ESU (European Size Units). Holdings in this size category occupy only 8% of the total crops and grass area of British agriculture and contribute less than 3% of the industry's total standard gross margin. At the other extreme, holdings rated at 40 ESU and above contribute more than half the total standard gross margin of the industry, but only 15% of OGA holdings are in this size range (Furness, 1983). The significance of part-time farming lies in the numbers of people involved rather than in its contribution to farm output.

Further analysis of the Labour Input Inquiry data showed that half the holdings where farmers had second jobs were rated below one annual work unit, which represents the labour input of one adult worker in a year. Together they accounted for only 16% of the total labour input to British agriculture. The Wye College survey estimated the total area in part-time farms to be just over two million ha, slightly more than one-sixth of the total agricultural area of England and Wales.

Part-time farmers in general operate on a smaller scale than full-timers, they have less time available for farming and they are not under the same pressure to expand output in order to maximize or even maintain their incomes. These tendencies are reflected in the choice of enterprises and the slower pace of technical change on the typical part-time farm. Table 9.3, derived from the 1983 Labour Input Inquiry, classifies farms by main enterprise. It shows that more than half of all part-time holdings specialize in extensive livestock enterprises like cattle and sheep as against 38% of

Table 9.2 Distribution of OGA holdings in England and Wales, 1983 by size measured in ESU.

Holding size in ESU	Number of OGA holdings (000s)	%	OGA holdings as % of all holdings
Under 4	21.1	40.2	48.0
4<8	8.9	16.9	44.8
8<16	7.1	13.5	32.3
16<40	7.7	14.7	20.1
40<100	5.3	10.0	15.1
100 and over	2.4	4.6	19.8
All OGA holdings	52.6	100.0	30.7

Source: MAFF, unpublished results of 1983 Labour Input Inquiry.

Table 9.3 Type of farming and farmer's main activity.

Type of farming	Farmers with other jobs		Farmers without other jobs
	major	minor	
		% of holdings	
Dairying	4.1	7.3	23.5
Cattle/sheep	59.7	52.9	37.5
Cropping	21.0	20.6	21.5
Pigs/poultry	4.1	3.9	3.6
Horticulture	6.1	8.0	5.2
Mixed	5.0	7.3	8.7
All types	100.0	100.0	100.0

Source: MAFF, provisional results of 1983 Labour Input Inquiry.

full-time farms. Dairying, a labour-demanding activity, is the main enterprise on 24% of full-time farms but less than 8% of all part-time farms and only 4% of those where the farmer's other activity is the main one. Part-time farmers are neither more nor less likely than full-timers to run cropping farms, slightly more likely to be involved in horticulture.

Besides being under less pressure than others to expand their businesses, farmers with second jobs may not be able to devote the necessary time to developing the farm business, which entails keeping abreast of technical progress, seeking professional advice, raising capital and managing change. Many cannot consider new developments which would increase the complexity of management or add to an already heavy workload. The way capital grant schemes are administered is another obstacle to change, since the applicant must devote more than half his time to farming the holding and derive more than half his income from it.

Evidence from the Wye College survey suggested that only just over half the part-time farms had made any significant capital improvement, under 40% a major change in the farming system and under 30% any change in holding size in the preceding five-year period. Change was more characteristic of the larger, 'main living' or Class I part-time farms (those mainly dependent on farm incomes) which tended to invest more heavily in permanent structures and installations, to purchase rather than sell land and to expand rather than contract enterprises. Where change had occurred on the smaller, Class II or 'supplementary income' farms, acreage gains were usually small, investment more often of the land-improving type and enterprises typically contracted or given up.

Implications for the rural population

By enabling families to remain on the land at an acceptable level of living, part-time farming has a certain influence on the size and composition of rural communities. It is reasonable to assume that the bulk of part-time farming households earning most of their income from other sources would not be able to stay in agriculture without those other occupations. It is likely, too, that many of the 'main living' farm households could not continue in farming without a second income source. Upwards of 40,000 families, at a very rough guess, might be able to remain living on farms by virtue of other sources of earned income. While this number seems very small in relation to the five million population normally resident in rural areas of England and Wales, it is not insignificant in relation to a total of some 180,000 main agricultural holdings.

If part-time farming enables some families to remain on the land who would otherwise have been forced, by low and declining farm incomes, to quit their farms and move elsewhere, it may equally enable other families to gain entry to agriculture. In view of the amount of capital required to set up in full-time commercial farming nowadays and the narrowing of opportunities for entry to the industry for those not born into farming families, more aspiring farmers may be obliged to take this route. In the United States today the majority of new entrants to farming begin on a small scale as part-time farmers (Lyson, 1984). Besides those who come to part-time farming via full-time farming or from non-farm occupations, there are families whose occupation of a farm has always been associated with some other business or employment.

The background of farmers and the route they take into part-time farming have significant implications for rural society. An influx of newcomers from non-farming backgrounds, who farm as a sideline while continuing to rely mainly on other sources of income, represents a more radical change for the farming community than the trend for established farmers and members of their families to seek additional employment off the farm. Members of the two groups will most probably differ in the way they approach the business of farming, in the kinds of decisions they take and the type of farming they practise. More fundamental differences in lifestyle and outlook may also divide them.

On the basis of the Wye College survey it was estimated that 55% of occupiers of OGA holdings in England and Wales in 1983 had begun their working careers on the land. (Dunn (1969) found similarly that 52% of occupiers of small holdings in Scotland had begun their careers in agriculture.) Nearly half the occupiers of OGA holdings, in other words, had entered farming from some other occupation, and this was especially pronounced in the more urbanized areas. Farmers who had begun their careers in agriculture were more prominent in the remoter rural areas.

The route the farmer had taken into part-time farming was found to be highly correlated with a number of farm and personal characteristics, suggesting that the part-time farming population is a mixture of diverse groups. At one extreme are those who began their working lives on the land and for whom farming is still the main occupation and source of income. These farmers occupy the larger holdings and are well represented in East Anglia and the north of England. At the other extreme, those for whom farming has never been more than a sideline, who entered farming from some other occupation which continues to provide the main source of income, are concentrated on the smallest holdings and are particularly prominent in south-east England.

The typical 'new entrant' type of part-time farmer lives on a small farm in the Home Counties, the Midlands or north-west England and commutes to a business or professional job in London, Manchester or Birmingham. His non-farming occupation provides a more than adequate living and running a farm business cannot be regarded as a financial necessity. Indeed, some of these farm households will feature among the 17% shown in Table 9.1 who combined high incomes from other sources with farming losses. Motives other than income are required to explain why they are farming. In many cases farming is valued for the lifestyle, a means of living in the country and enjoying peace and quiet, an escape from the stresses of city life. It provides a new and absorbing interest, an activity which all members of the family can share, a wholesome environment in which to raise children. Besides these non-pecuniary considerations, occupying a farm may be a means of securing wealth for future generations; farmers in this category almost always own the land and would have seen their investment appreciate considerably during the 1970s.

At the opposite end of the farm size spectrum are operators of large and successful farm businesses who nevertheless engage in some supplementary activity. Often this will be a second business located on the farm and linked with it in some way. Agricultural contractors, farm management consultants, farm tourist entrepreneurs, food processors, agricultural engineers, cattle dealers and feed merchants are typical examples. Enterprises involving farm work elsewhere are particularly prominent in Yorkshire, farm-based recreation and tourism in the south-west, northern England and Wales and other businesses on the farm, in the Midlands and north-west. Typically the farmer has seized an opportunity to make use of some spare resource on the farm or to develop a successful farm-related business beyond the holding. Profitability may be the driving force but it is not necessarily the only consideration. The need to meet a challenge or develop a new interest may also be influential here. Sometimes the other occupation is the province of the farmer's wife who feels the need for a career of her own, to develop an identity apart from that of housewife and mother. The fact that many wives on large farms, notably in south-west England, are involved in catering for visitors, can be explained in these terms (Bouquet, 1985).

A third and perhaps more heterogeneous category consists of part-time farming families who have neither chosen to enter farming in order to experience the lifestyle nor deliberately grasped the opportunity to utilize spare resources in the farm business. This includes those who have never been able to make an adequate income from farming alone and those recently forced into that situation by rising costs and falling returns. Typically they operate farms in the middle band, too small to yield an acceptable living by current standards yet too large to be run as spare-time enterprises in conjunction with another full-time job. These farmers may not be well placed to set up alternative businesses on the farm. Where shortages of capital or land are limiting the development of the farm business, it is unlikely that these resources would be available to start another enterprise. Furthermore, if the need to supplement farm income stems from ineffective business management, it is unlikely that the farmer would be more successful in managing an alternative enterprise where market orientation is even more critical for success (Slee, 1987).

Consistent with this typology is the discovery that lowest incomes occur in the middle of the farm size range. The 10% of part-time farming households identified in Table 9.1 as having combined earnings of less than £4,000 in 1983/4, were disproportionately represented in the middle band. In the United States, too, highest non-farm earnings are found to be associated with the smallest and largest farms (see for instance Larson, 1975; USDA, 1984), a pattern previously described for OECD countries (OECD, 1978).

In very broad terms, then, combining farming with some other paid activity is likely to represent a choice on the part of those on larger farms who could make a living from farming alone and those on small holdings with adequate incomes from other sources. By contrast some of those on small to middle-sized, marginalized holdings are being forced, unwillingly, to seek additional employment.

Trends in part-time farming

According to the OECD study, part-time farming is increasing in the world's highly developed countries, particularly among the smaller farms. In countries where the situation has been monitored over time, the tendency has been for the number of 'supplementary income' or Class II part-time farms to increase relative to 'main living' or Class I part-time and full-time farms. This implies both an increase in the proportion of part-time farms and an increase in the value of non-farm relative to farm income flows.

Evidence from a number of industrialized countries supports the suggestion that other sources of income are becoming increasingly important for farm households. The share of farm family income in the

United States originating from non-farm sources, for instance, was 26% in 1945, 40% in 1960 and over 60% by the mid-1980s (Carlin and Ghelfi, 1979; Ahearn *et al.*, 1985). Off-farm income as a proportion of total income of the Canadian farm population rose from 12% in 1940 to 59% in 1970 (Shaw, 1979). The average Swedish farm family derived 37% of its income from other sources in 1966, 68% in 1980 (Persson, 1983) while corresponding figures for Japan were 45% in 1960 and 75% by 1979 (Kada, 1982).

No comparable data are available for Britain but a crude indication of trends can be obtained by comparing results of the 1983 Structure Survey and the Wye College survey with those of the 1941/3 National Farm Survey (Ministry of Agriculture and Fisheries, 1946). In the earlier survey all agricultural holdings of 5 acres (2 ha) and above were classified according to 'economic type of occupier'. 'Full-time' occupiers had no other gainful activity. 'Part-time' occupiers, corresponding to Class I households, relied mainly on farming for their living but drew additional income from other sources. The 1941/3 survey also identified 'spare-time' occupiers who farmed as a source of income but had some other main employment, and 'hobby and other' farmers who occupied land for convenience or pleasure rather than for profit. As a rough approximation, Class II part-time farms in the later survey were divided into those reporting a positive farm income before tax in 1983/4 (Class IIa) and those reporting a loss or no profit (Class IIb).

Farm income data for one year are not a reliable basis for a classification and too much should not be read into Table 9.4. Nevertheless, the broad trends appear to be in line with those in other developed countries. The total number of holdings to which the 1983 Labour Input Inquiry referred was little more than half the number covered in the 1941/3 National Farm survey, due mainly to small holdings being excluded from

Table 9.4 Classification of agricultural holdings in England and Wales by economic type of occupier in 1941/3 and main source of household income in 1983/4.

Economic type 1941/3	Number 000s	%	Income class 1983/4	Number 000s	%	Percentage change
Full-time	216	74.3	Full-time	119	69.3	−45
Part-time	33	11.2	Part-time Class I	18	10.6	−44
Spare-time	28	9.8	Part-time Class IIa	18	10.5	−37
Hobby/other	14	4.7	Part-time Class IIb	16	9.5	+18
All holdings	291	100.0		170	100.0	−41

Sources: MAFF, National Farm Survey 1941/3; MAFF, unpublished results of 1983 Labour Input Inquiry; Wye College survey.

the agricultural census, being absorbed into larger units or going out of agricultural use. While this should have had the effect of removing many part-time units, the proportion of holdings farmed on a part-time basis actually rose from 26 to 31% of the total. The most likely explanation must be that part-time farming has encroached on what were formerly full-time farms. The last column of Table 9.4 suggests that Class II part-time farms have been increasing relative to Class I and full-time farms in England and Wales, echoing experience in other OECD countries. More tentatively it can be suggested that the growth of the Class IIb type of part-time farming household, occupying land for convenience or pleasure rather than for profit, has been responsible for the overall increase in part-time farming. While numbers of full-time and Class I part-time farms have been almost halved, numbers in Class IIb have risen by nearly one-fifth.

Predictions and consequences

Economic pressures are expected to hasten the trend towards part-time farming in Britain in the foreseeable future. In whatever way the crisis of over-production and over-spending in the European Community is resolved, it is unlikely to become any easier to make a living from farming alone and will probably be more difficult. Conditions will therefore favour those who are able to supplement their farm incomes from other sources. Households on progressively larger farms will give serious thought to alternatives and many more will diversify their activities. The setting up of agriculturally related second businesses on the farm is being encouraged by the Farm Diversification Grants Scheme and this option is likely to appeal particularly to those on larger farms with land or farm buildings surplus to present needs, access to capital and a flair for spotting and exploiting some new opportunity (Slee, 1987).

Diversification of activity on the farm is not the answer for every farm business. On the smaller farm where family labour rather than land or capital is in surplus, the solution may lie in off-farm employment for the farmer or another member of the household. Limiting factors are likely to include a shortage of suitable jobs in rural areas, long distances to travel, lack of appropriate qualifications and skills among farm family members and an excessive workload if the farming system is not adjusted to allow for the reduction in the labour force. Here it seems probable that farm families who already have other sources of earned income will be better placed to survive a period of falling farm incomes than those who have yet to break into the non-farm labour market.

Whilst diversifying activities on the farm and seeking additional off-farm employment can be seen as a transition for the existing farm population, the entry of newcomers who make farming a subsidiary activity right from the outset, represents more of a transformation. A growth in personal incomes, housing pressure in the southern half of England and falling land prices are all likely to fuel the trend. The influx of new families with different objectives in farming, different backgrounds and skills and a different outlook on life is likely to have a much greater impact on rural communities than the more gradual transition from full- to part-time farming.

Finally, increasing concern over the rural environment may reinforce or be reinforced by the swing towards Class II part-time farming. The farmer who does not have to depend wholly on farming for a living can afford to follow farming practices more 'friendly' to the environment. He is under less pressure to expand the area of his holding, make capital improvements or intensify production, changes which are generally felt to threaten the environment. Part-time farms carry few enterprises, with a marked emphasis on grazing cattle, sheep and horses, and are not likely to exacerbate the surplus problem. Indeed, part-time farming is seen to be quite compatible with the goals of extensification, cereal set-aside and diversification which the government is currently promoting through its socio-structural policy.

References

Ahearn, M., Johnson, J. and Strickland, R. (1985) The distribution of income and wealth of farm operator households. *American Journal of Agricultural Economics*, **67**, 1087–94.

Arkleton Trust (1985) *Part-time Farming in the Rural Development of Industrialized Countries*. The Arkleton Trust, Langholm.

Bouquet, M. (1985) *Family, Servants and Visitors*. Geo Books, Norwich.

Carlin, T.A. and Ghelfi, L.M. (1979) Off-farm employment and the farm sector. In: *Structure Issues of American Agriculture*. US Government Printing Office, Washington, DC, pp. 270–3.

Dunn, J.M. (1969) Some features of small full-time and large part-time farms in Scotland. *Scottish Agricultural Economics*, **xix**, 205–20.

Furness, G.W. (1983) The importance, distribution and net incomes of small farm businesses in the UK. In: Tranter, R.B. (ed.), *Strategies for Family-worked Farms in the UK*. University of Reading Centre for Agricultural Strategy, pp. 12–41.

Gasson, R. (1988) *The Economics of Part-time Farming*. Longman, London.

Kada, R. (1982) Trends and characteristics of part-time farming in post-war Japan. *GeoJournal*, **6**, 367–71.

Larson, D.K. (1975) Economic class as a measure of farmers' welfare. *American Journal of Agricultural Economics*, **57**, 658–64.

Lyson, T.A. (1984) Pathways into production agriculture: the structuring of farm recruitment in the United States. In: Schwarzweller, H.K. (ed.), *Focus on Agriculture*. JAI Press, Greenwich, Conn., pp. 79–103.

Ministry of Agriculture and Fisheries (1946) *National Farm Survey of England and Wales 1941–1943. A Summary Report*. HMSO, London.

Organisation for Economic Co-operation and Development (1978) *Part-time Farming in OECD Countries: General Report*. OECD, Paris.

Persson, L.O. (1983) Part time farming – cornerstone or obstacle in rural development? *Sociologia Ruralis*, **xxiii**, 50–62.

Robson, N. (1987) The changing role of part-time farming in the structure of agriculture. *Journal of Agricultural Economics*, **xxxviii**, 168–75.

Shaw, P.R. (1979) Canadian farm and nonfarm family incomes. *American Journal of Agricultural Economics*, **61**, 676–82.

Slee, B. (1987) *Alternative Farm Enterprises*. Farming Press, Ipswich.

United States Department of Agriculture (1984) *Economic Indicators of the Farm Sector*. USDA, Washington DC.

Chapter 10
British Agricultural Policy and the EC

Edmund Neville-Rolfe

(Editor's Note: Maintaining the point of view expressed in Chapter 1 that 'any attempt to look into the future must begin with an appreciation of where we are now, and of how we arrived here', the author of this chapter surveys in some detail the negotiations for Britain's entry into the European Community and the significance of membership for British agriculture, before taking a look at some prospects for the future. The thread running through the chapter is the question: how far can the Common Agricultural Policy be expected to mould, or be moulded by, developments in British agriculture? It is a question which it would be presumptuous to try to answer without regard to the historical antecedents of the present situation.)

The 1961–63 negotiations for entry

The difficulties faced by the British negotiators in obtaining satisfactory terms for the country's accession to the European Economic Community were almost all concerned, directly or indirectly, with agriculture. They encapsulate the changes which adoption of the Community's Common Agricultural Policy (CAP) was to require to the policies for food and agriculture which successive British governments had been following since the end of the Second World War: largely duty-free imports of the principal commodities, with preference to those from the Commonwealth; guaranteed producer prices supported by means of deficiency payments; and strict Parliamentary control over the agricultural budget – all these would have to go. During the abortive negotiation which got under way in February 1962 and ended with General de Gaulle's veto in January 1963, well over half the time spent round the conference table was devoted to an attempt to ensure for Commonwealth exporters of cereals outlets to the enlarged Community comparable to those which they had traditionally enjoyed in trade with Britain.

The priority given to this part of the negotiation resulted from an undertaking given by the government to Parliament in response to the strong pressure applied by Canada, Australia and New Zealand. The

Commonwealth interest also received powerful support from British public opinion, for reasons both of sentiment and of concern for the effect of the Community's protectionist policies on food prices.

In the event the British were able to obtain no more than a temporary relaxation of the principle of 'Community preference'. That principle, as applied by the original Six, had ensured that the common price within the Community was above that of competing imports, which of course included those from the Commonwealth and other traditional suppliers of the UK market. The Six had already arranged, after protracted negotiations among themselves, to set a minimum import price (or 'threshold' price) in relation to an internal 'target' price which eventually turned out to be about midway between the traditionally high level of support enjoyed by farmers in Germany and the price – lower by over 20% – then being paid by the French government to its (more efficient) cereal growers. This agreed internal price level for cereals was a key factor in determining the common level of support for all other arable products, and most livestock products, within the CAP (Neville-Rolfe, 1984).

The British request for accession to the Community was formally tabled by Edward Heath, then Lord Privy Seal and chief negotiator, in October 1961. However, on French insistence the Six were determined that any consideration of the agricultural aspects of British accession should await the outcome of their own debate on how the CAP would be financed, and on the form which the common market organizations (CMOs) for the various major commodities would take. Agreement on these matters, and on the next stage of the dismantling of internal industrial tariffs which had been tied into the same timetable by the Treaty, was not reached until 14 January 1962, but any expectations which the British may have had of influencing the basic forms of support for agriculture (variable levies on imports and internal purchase by the authorities of any grain of appropriate quality offered to them at an 'intervention price') were disappointed.

Once the negotiations on the terms of British entry were able to begin, even those Member States most favourable to the accession of Britain were unwilling to risk re-opening the very difficult debate on the basic mechanism of the CAP. Instead, the negotiation was confined to finding mutually acceptable means of moving, during a relatively short transitional period, from British policy mechanisms to those already adopted by the Community. In their role as *demandeurs* the British found themselves in no position to insist on any fundamental changes to the basic principles of the CAP, as exemplified in the cereals market regulation.

The British government's freedom to manoeuvre was also constrained by undertakings given in Parliament and elsewhere to maintain the long-term guarantees given to farmers by the Agriculture Acts of 1947 and 1957. Because these were well-established but would have to undergo substantial change, the claim was put forward that British farmers would require a longer transitional period than had been granted to farmers in the Six, but this was not accepted by the existing members, who pointed to the greatly superior structure of British farms – as they have done on many subsequent occasions. Nor were they disposed to concede that deficiency payments – the vital feature of the British system of farm support – could continue to be paid by the British government, even on a degressive basis, during the period when internal market prices in the UK would be rising from their currently low 'world' level to the much higher (though not firmly pre-determined) level which would result from full application of the CAP regulations.

After almost a year of negotiation, the only agricultural issue on which the Six had made some concession to the British point of view was the maintenance of an Annual Review procedure – an issue particularly cherished by the National Farmers Union. But, even here, the holding of national Annual Reviews was not to be made mandatory, nor could the decisions taken at any national review be binding on the Commission which, under the Treaty, is the sole initiator of legislative proposals.

When General de Gaulle gave as one reason for rejecting the application of the British to join the European Community his perception that their gaze was still fixed *au grand large* – out to sea – he will have had in mind not only the claim to a 'special relationship' with the USA (which had recently been re-affirmed by Harold Macmillan and President Kennedy at Nassau) but also the preference still given by the UK to the Commonwealth and its exports of food and raw materials. He seems not to have been convinced that the British agreement to abandon after a short transitional period an agricultural policy based very largely on that preference represented a real change of heart.

The 1970–72 negotiations

It was not until 1970 – nine years after Edward Heath's request for accession – that General de Gaulle's successor, President Georges Pompidou, so far modified France's European policies as to agree to a re-opening of the negotiations for Britain's entry. Once again the success or failure of those negotiations was to depend crucially on agricultural issues. Two of these had been prominent on the previous agenda – access for the Commonwealth and transitional arrangements for British agriculture; but now a third issue, the financing of the CAP, which had hitherto intruded only marginally, because of major significance.

By this time the situation had been reached that the establishment of common market regulations covering all the major agricultural product groups was now virtually complete. As far as access for Commonwealth supplies was concerned, by 1970 cereals were no longer an issue. It was realized by the British that no preference for imports from Australia or

Canada was likely to be negotiable. Those countries would have to take their chance with others in competing to surmount the Community's variable levy system in supplying what would still, after enlargement, be a deficit area, especially for maize and for the North American hard wheats required by British millers.

Instead, negotiations were concentrated in two areas: sugar and dairy products. As in the case of cereals in the earlier negotiations, the British government was under strong pressure from Commonwealth countries, supported by public opinion in Britain, to preserve access for their exports to the enlarged Community, or at any rate to the UK. The arguments were not only economic but also moral. The countries of the Caribbean and of the Pacific which currently benefited from the Commonwealth Sugar Agreement were, apart from Australia, poor, underdeveloped and heavily dependent on sugar exports for their livelihood. New Zealand, whose exports of dairy products and lamb were a vital element in its foreign trade, aroused in Britain strong feelings of sentiment and kinship, supported by the memory of its contribution to allied victory in two world wars.

On the other hand, there was a powerful European sugar beet lobby, led by the French, while the dairy industry of the Six regarded Britain as a future and legitimate outlet for its products, especially butter (already a surplus in the community).

Access for Commonwealth cane sugar exports was eventually assured by a painstakingly negotiated formula, contained in a declaration to be attached to the Treaty, whereby the enlarged Community would 'have as its firm purpose' (*aurait à coeur*) the safeguarding of the interests of those countries whose economies were heavily dependent on sugar production. This undertaking came to be honoured in the Protocol to the Lomé Convention which guaranteed to the cane sugar-producing states associated with the Community a preferential quota equivalent to 1.3 million tonnes of refined sugar.

In the absence, at that time, of any common market regulation relating to sheepmeat, confrontation with the Six over the question of New Zealand lamb was avoided. Later, in 1981, the British government was able to obtain terms which were favourable to both British and New Zealand producers. The issue of New Zealand dairy products, on the other hand, was not resolved until the summer of 1971 as part of a trade-off between Britain and France relating to the British contribution to the budget.

Early on in these 1970–2 negotiations two things became clear. First, Britain could not expect a longer transitional period for agricultural adaptation to the new market situation than was being granted in relation to industrial products. Second, Britain would have to adhere forthwith to the Community regulations relating to the operation of the CAP. In order to protect the interests of British consumers, however, the transition to the high level of Community agricultural support prices would be made by equal annual steps over a five-year period. Following the devaluation of sterling in 1967, Community support prices were now substantially higher in sterling terms than the prices guaranteed to British farmers under the deficiency payments system.

There was no longer any question of trying to negotiate for British farmers a continuation of the long-term assurances to which they were accustomed, and the NFU exerted much less pressure in that direction. As regards arrangements for an Annual Review on the British pattern, the Community had gone no further than to agree in 1963 that regular consultation should take place with COPA (the European organization of national farmers' associations); and it had to be recognized that the effectiveness of COPA might be weakened rather than strengthened by the need to reach unanimity between nine national points of view instead of six.

The only attempt to graft British policy on to that of the Community which met with any notable degree of success was to be the institution in 1975 of the 'less favoured areas' Directive, which borrowed a number of ideas from the long-standing special aids to hill farmers in the UK.

The troublesome question of Britain's disproportionate contribution to the EC budget was to preoccupy the Community for almost 15 years. By 1962 it had already become evident that the cost of financing the CAP was likely to be unduly burdensome for a Member State such as Britain with a generally low level of self-sufficiency in the principal agricultural products. The scope for taking advantage of sales into intervention, or for obtaining refunds (*réstitutions*) on exports to third countries, would be more limited than in the case of Member States disposing of surpluses. This meant that no great part of the Guarantee Section of the European Agricultural Guidance and Guarantee Fund (generally known by its French acronym FEOGA) would be received by the UK. Under the Guidance Section drawings would also be limited because of Britain's generally favourable structure of farm sizes and of agricultural processing and marketing facilities.

As regards payments towards the cost of the budget, on the other hand, Britain would have substantial contributions to make in the form of levies and duties on agricultural imports, duties on industrial imports and the obligatory 1% (as it then was) of the yield of the national Value Added Tax.

Some attempts at this time by the British to establish a principle of 'fair shares' met with little sympathy, least of all from the French, who also strongly resisted the making of any concessions on the rate of increase of the British contribution during the transitional period. The final deal in these negotiations, reached in June 1971, fixed both the starting percentage and the ultimate level of the UK's contribution a good deal higher than had been proposed in the British negotiators' opening bid, but still much lower than the French would have wished. Since it was to take another four months of negotiation to reach agreement on the Common Fisheries Policy, the Treaty of Accession was not signed until January 1972.

The 're-negotiation' of the Treaty of Accession

Only a minority of the Parliamentary Labour party had voted in favour of the terms negotiated by the Conservative government in 1971–72, and Harold Wilson was returned to office in March 1974 with an election pledge to 're-negotiate' the terms of the Accession Treaty. The new government's objectives would be to reduce the cost of the CAP, to ensure that the UK would not be required to shoulder a disproportionate share of the Community budget, to improve some of the marketing arrangements, notably for beef, and to secure improved access for foodstuffs from third countries. The terms negotiated would then be submitted to a national referendum.

The principal measure negotiated by the Minister of Agriculture was a so-called variable premium for beef – in effect, a deficiency payment. Although all Member States were free to adopt this system as a partial substitute for sales into intervention, none except Britain ever chose to do so. Apart from the aids to hill farmers, this was the only measure of essentially British origin which found its way into the CAP. The same kind of provision was to be extended to sheepmeat when regulations for that product were eventually introduced in 1981.

As regards improved access for third country produce, the Heads of Government at their Dublin summit meeting of March 1975 confirmed that access for New Zealand butter would be continued after the end of the transitional period in 1977. Also, the Lomé Convention of 1976 would honour the pledge to the developing countries of the Commonwealth, that they would have access for their sugar.

As for Britain's contribution to the EC budget, the Dublin summit meeting agreed on a formula linking the level of that contribution to a number of macro-economic indices. The constraints written into the agreement were, however, such that it was to prove inoperative, and the whole issue was destined to be re-opened even more vehemently at a later date.

The other objective of the Wilson government's 're-negotiation' – reducing the cost of agricultural support – was fortuitously assisted by the publication of the EC Commission's *Stocktaking of the CAP* (Commission, 1975a), drawn up at the insistence of the government of the Federal Republic of Germany. This put forward a series of proposals, including measures to reduce budgetary expenditure. Many of them were not new, but the British government, in presenting them as being wholly in line with its own views, was able to reinforce the argument for acceptance of the re-negotiated settlement, which duly received a two-thirds majority of those voting in the referendum in June 1975.

The consequences of accession

Any hopes which the antimarketeers in both the Conservative and Labour parties might have had that the UK would withdraw from the Community were effectively extinguished by the verdict of the referendum. Britain was now committed to a reversal of its traditional policies for trade in food-stuffs, market pricing and support measures for farmers. Successive Ministers of Agriculture have done no more than attempt, by their use of their vote in the Council, and with the help of any allies they could find there, to promote what used to be the three axioms of British agricultural policy: concern for the consumer's interests; the minimum of protection against imports; and constraint on public spending. Their protestations have been largely an exercise in damage limitation, whether by seeking to prevent large institutional price increases or devaluations of the 'green' pound, resisting proposals for a tax on oils and fats, or pressing for greater 'budgetary discipline'.

The significance of the CAP for Britain

The Community's original concept of common agricultural 'institutional' prices denominated in units of account, to which each Member State's currency bore a fixed relationship, disappeared in the international monetary upheavals of the early 1970s. The establishment of the European Monetary System (EMS) and the European currency unit (ECU) in 1979 restored some degree of stability. Nevertheless there has continued to be a need for a number of Member States to maintain at any one time a so-called 'green' exchange rate for trade in the principal agricultural products distinct from the central rate fixed between each national currency and the ECU. A country's green rate may be temporarily differentiated from its currency's central rate according to whether a Member State's government requires to maintain an overvalued green rate for the benefit of its farmers or an undervalued one for the benefit of its consumers. Normally Member States revaluing their central rates against the ECU – essentially the German Federal Republic, but occasionally the Netherlands and others – have been reluctant to revalue their green rates in parallel since this involves a reduction in national currency terms of the common support prices expressed in ECU. Devaluing countries, on the other hand, have usually been much readier to undertake devaluations of their green currencies and thus raise support prices in national currency terms for their farmers without undue concern for the effect on food prices for their consumers. This has been a particularly useful device for reducing the effects of the severe price restraint made necessary in recent years by the runaway budget expenditure on agricultural support.

In order to mitigate the potential distortions to the supposedly common price system caused by these differentiated exchange rates, monetary compensatory amounts (MCAs) are charged at national frontiers. For revaluing countries so-called 'positive' MCAs represent a subsidy on exports and a tax on imports. For devaluing countries 'negative' MCAs represent a subsidy on imports and a tax on exports. Positive German MCAs have been brought about by successive revaluations of the Deutschmark in relation to the Community's weaker currencies. Their dismantling has posed considerable political difficulties for Federal governments, whose electoral prospects have, for various reasons, usually depended on the support of the farm vote.

In marked contrast to other Member States with relatively weak currencies British governments have generally been reluctant to dismantle the negative MCAs that have resulted from the weakness of sterling. The level of these MCAs has been affected by governments' choice to remain outside the EMS (and its predecessor the European 'snake') and maintain a floating rate for sterling. Instead of representing as in the case of France, say, a fixed relationship between its central and green rates, the British negative MCA has fluctuated from week to week according to changes in the average market rate of sterling in relation to the basket of EMS currencies (or of the earlier 'snake'). An appreciation of sterling may reduce the MCA, or even, as it did briefly during the early 1980s, convert it into a positive one. But, however large the increase in the negative MCA, governments of both parties have generally chosen to maintain the benefit to the consumer, and to the general rate of inflation, of the subsidy on food imports which it represents. Formal, usually modest, devaluations of the green pound, for the benefit of farmers, have been confined to the general adjustment of green rates which usually accompanies the Community's annual price review. Like German governments, though for quite opposite reasons, British governments have resisted pressure from the EC Commission to adapt their green rates to any greater extent than was consistent with their own interests. This is one important respect in which they have retained some freedom of action within the CAP (Neville-Rolfe, 1984).

British Ministers of Agriculture have had rather less success in promoting a policy of price restraint. Even when such a policy has been urged by the Commission, as it was in the late 1970s and has been since the re-emergence of the Community's budgetary crisis in 1983, British support for the Commission, usually seconded by the Dutch, has not on the whole succeeded in persuading the majority of its partners to accept the full rigour of the Commission's proposals. In any case British opposition to increases in farm price support, however well principled, has been seen to be not entirely disinterested. Not only does Britain not obtain any net gain from expenditure on the CAP, but the weakness of sterling has usually made it possible for British farmers to be compensated for any price cuts or freezes by means of discreet devaluations of the green pound. On the one occasion, in 1982, on which a British Minister of Agriculture, Peter

Walker, attempted to veto an annual price package on the grounds of 'vital national interest' he was heavily outvoted. The other ministers argued, correctly, that the proposed price increases – very generous ones as it happened – could not in themselves be considered a threat to British interests. Indeed the Minister seemed to be prepared to go along with most of them. His veto was merely being used to put pressure on the Council of Foreign Ministers to agree to the level of budgetary rebates at that time being demanded by Britain over the following three years. All the price increases were duly voted through by the necessary qualified majority of Agriculture Ministers, thus exhibiting a degree of imprudence which, coming after a price settlement the year before of almost equal generosity, was to help raise expenditure on agriculture to unprecedented levels, and involve the Community in an almost continuous state of budgetary crisis (Neville-Rolfe, 1984).

Although it originated in the disproportionate share of agriculture in Community expenditure, to follow the course of the long-running debate over Britain's net contribution to the budget lies outside the scope of an account of the impact of the CAP on British agricultural policy. It may even seem paradoxical that in a work dealing with the future of British farming so much space should have been devoted, as far as policy is concerned, to the recent past. But it is important to stress the reasons for the limitations imposed by membership of the European Community on any British Minister of Agriculture for taking autonomous decisions both now and in the future. Nevertheless, recent changes of direction in the CAP will somewhat extend the scope for national initiatives.

The significance for Britain of the three pillars of the CAP

Community preference

Although there is no specific mention of them in the Rome Treaty there emerged during the 1960s a concept of the three pillars of the CAP: Community preference, common prices and common financing. Any assessment of the CAP's future needs to test their strength. Community preference involves the view that farmers should be protected against imports that compete in price with their own produce on the internal market. The variable levy system which operates for the majority of animal and plant products (with the notable exception of oilseeds) has ensured a minimal level of third country imports (often confined to negotiated quotas) and in some cases their virtual exclusion. Other restrictive forms of minimum import price apply in the case of fruit and vegetables. The system has been reinforced in two ways: first, as already noted, by the initially high level of price support for cereals, from which most other prices have been derived; and second by the subsidizing of exports by means of so-called refunds that bridge the gap between the common threshold price and the normally lower world price. One objective of the Commission's repeated efforts to lower the level of price support has been to reduce the unit cost, and consequently the budgetary burden, of refunds, especially in the conditions of low world prices caused by oversupply, the aggressive export policy of the United States, and the weakness of the dollar which character-ized the late 1980s. A reduction in threshold prices could also represent some earnest of the Community's willingness to pursue a more liberal trade policy in the context of the Uruguay Round of multilateral trade negoti-ations. The notable absence of preference in relation to imports of oilseeds, and of other products which may be used as a substitute for cereals in animal feed, most of which enter the Community at nil or low rates of duty bound in the General Agreement on Tariffs and Trade (GATT), has been a perennial source of complaint by cereal producers, and, in the case of oilseeds, of a mounting budgetary cost of the deficiency payment system of internal price support. Any unbinding and raising of these rates of import duty would, under GATT rules, have to be compensated by some relax-ation of Community preference elsewhere. For example, this might take the form of relaxing the variable levy system by introducing fixed tariff quotas for a certain volume of cereals.

Any abandonment of Community preference must be seen as politically out of the question. Incidentally, its British critics should not forget that already in the years leading up to the entry of the UK into the Community quantitative import restrictions on butter and bacon, based on so-called voluntary restraint on the part of Britain's main suppliers, were introduced, as well as import levies on cereals. In the face of rising domestic productivity protection, with the purpose of limiting exchequer expenditure on deficiency payments, had to be accepted in principle. It is the level rather than the principle of the Community's preference that is open to criticism and the source of protest by its principal trading partners.

Common prices

The shakiness of the CAP's second pillar, common prices, is evident from the absence of monetary stability and the need to introduce parallel green rates of exchange to compensate for the periodic realignment of national currencies. But even if, in the absence of monetary union, common prices when translated into national currencies have no common value, they will continue to be fixed centrally by the Council of Ministers at its traditional annual horse-trading sessions. Hitherto the degree of price restraint shown by Ministers has been largely a function of the state of the Community's finances. Over the years only the threatened exhaustion of the budget has tended to concentrate their minds sufficiently for them to adopt the 'prudent' or 'rigorous' price policies proposed by the Commission, and then usually in a watered down form. By 1984 the need for greater budgetary resources than had been originally allocated by the Six in 1970 became acute. The rising cost of financing the CAP was limiting the resources available for other policies for improving the infrastructure of the Community's less-developed regions, for alleviating mass unemployment, or for promoting research into new technologies.

A 40% increase in the proportion of the yield of VAT contributed to the budget by Member States was agreed by the Heads of Government at their Fontainebleau summit in June 1984. This was only secured on the condition, insisted on largely by the British, of strict budgetary discipline in the future. A new procedure required that, within a budget 'envelope' fixed annually, any increase in expenditure on agricultural market support must not exceed the rate of increase in the Community's total resources. Should any overrun of this limit occur it would have to be subtracted from the permissible increase in expenditure during the following two budget years. However, this rule could be waived in 'exceptional circumstances', thus leaving a large loophole in the principle of budgetary discipline. The over-runs which occurred every year between 1984 and 1988 were excused by two such circumstances: the fall in the value of the dollar which magnified the cost of subsidizing exports, and the need to liquidate at huge financial cost the accumulated intervention stocks of cereals, beef and dairy products.

Thus, neither the new resources nor the disciplinary procedures proved effective. Since deficit budgeting is not permitted by the Community's financial rules, bankruptcy was only avoided by a series of hand-to-mouth expedients, involving the transfer of payments from one fiscal year to the next, and in 1985 of a once-off special injection of national funds. When during 1987 the Commission put forward proposals for a further increase in resources, but on a revised and long-term basis, it was well aware of the need for more adequate safeguards if the principal contributing Member States, and particularly Britain, were to be persuaded to agree to the increase. Pluri-annual expenditure forecasts were shown to be containable within the proposed new ceiling. In order to ensure the necessary constraints to expenditure on agricultural market support the Commission proposed that mandatory 'stabilizers' (that is, price and other penalties for exceeding certain output ceilings) should be reinforced for the whole range of products subject to a CMO. Guarantee thresholds (limits to quantities eligible for price support) would be introduced where these did not already apply. Support for fat cattle and for sheep would be reduced. Particularly restrictive measures were proposed for cereals, being now, since the intro-duction of milk quotas in 1984, the most serious source of new surpluses, and for oilseeds, another major source of additional budgetary expenditure (Commission, 1987a).

Although in making these proposals the Commission envisaged no departure from the principle of common prices – price penalties would be applied across the board – it was also extending the concept of physical restraint on output. 'Stabilizers' are a convenient new jargon word for measures originally introduced for cereals in 1981 and subsequently applied to a number of other products, including oilseeds and tomato concentrate. In relating price to the level of output they resemble the 'standard quantities' applied to milk, and briefly to cereals, and the 'moving band' arrangements for fat pigs which were introduced in the UK in the 1960s as a means of adjusting supply to demand. They implicitly recognize that surpluses – in the sense of production that exceeds what can be utilized within the Community or exported commercially – arise not only from the assurance to farmers of unnecessarily attractive prices, but also from the diffusion and application of new technologies. By lowering unit costs of production these have made it possible for some farmers to increase their gross margins even at a lower level of prices.

Milk and cereals provide the most striking examples. Despite a virtually static cow population average yields per cow in the Community increased to an extent that price restraint alone proved insufficient to check the flow of milk to dairies. In 1984 Ministers were therefore obliged in the end to adopt the quota regime first proposed by the Commission three years earlier. Thanks to their customary reluctance to accept the full rigour of the Commission's proposals output was insufficiently reduced and intervention stocks of butter and skim powder rose to unprecedented levels of over a million tonnes each. Within another three years it therefore became necessary to reduce total quotas by almost 10% and generally tighten up the system. At the same time severe restrictions were placed on intervention sales. The Commission's stabilizer package adopted by the Council in February 1988 provided that the quota system, initially introduced for a five-year period, should be extended to 1991. Thereafter the Commission envisages that quotas should become more closely linked to dairies than to individual producers, 'thus encouraging the erosion of the artificial market value of quotas generated with the present system.' However, it seems unlikely that Ministers will readily consent to any change in the system that would deprive producers of what has, particularly in the UK, become a substantial capital asset, in some cases even doubling the value of the land to which the quotas are attached. At all events experience elsewhere, notably in Canada and Switzerland, suggests that once introduced milk quotas become a permanent feature of agricultural policy.

The tightening up of the quota system in 1987 had a marked impact. Reduced deliveries of milk and severe restrictions on sales into intervention had the intended effect of penalizing dairies which had long relied on disposing of much of their butter production into intervention. Several butter-making plants in England and Wales had to be closed. In a number of Member States producers who, thanks to permitted loopholes in the system, had been able to exceed their quotas with relative impunity found themselves obliged to cut back deliveries or face heavy fines. One long-term consequence of the stricter application of quotas will be a smaller supply of calves and cull cows. In view of the prevalence of dual purpose breeds and the widespread consumption of cowbeef in the Community, supplies of beef will be constricted and the risk of a re-emergence of the high levels of intervention stocks, which rose to over 800,000 tonnes in 1986/87, much reduced. Intervention buying of beef will in any case be virtually suspended, and the variable premiums (deficiency payments), 'renegotiated' by Britain in 1975, and jealously defended by successive Ministers of Agriculture ever since, have been finally phased out.

The similar premium for fat lambs is being phased out by 1992. Budgetary support has been fairly generous for sheepmeat, of which EC-10 had a relatively low degree of self-sufficiency. The size of the Spanish flock, however, and the potential for increased sheep pasture as a substitute for very low-yielding cereals in large areas of Portugal, suggest that the Community market could become oversupplied in future. Consequently a limit has been placed not only on the total number of ewes eligible for the ewe premium (18.1 million in the case of the UK), but also on the numbers eligible for the full rate of premium in individual flocks.

As far as other livestock products are concerned, support for poultry-meat and eggs will continue to be confined to protection against low-priced imports combined with subsidized exports, but after the Uruguay Round they could be on a less generous scale. Pigmeat is similarly protected, but the periodic aid given to private storage at times of oversupply has not prevented the persistence of the price cycles which traditionally afflict pig production. Intra-Community trade has in addition been greatly distorted by the operation of MCAs, which, there being no intervention price set for pigmeat, are based on its notional cereal content. At times of glut this has proved especially disadvantageous to importing Member States with weak currencies, notably France and Britain, whose negative MCAs act as an additional subsidy to exporting countries with stronger currencies such as Denmark and the Netherlands. Since Dutch producers rely heavily on feeding cereal 'substitutes' imported in bulk through Rotterdam at low or nil rates of duty, to apply MCAs for pigmeat linked to the intervention price for cereals is seen as additionally unreasonable. Although political pressures within the Council of Ministers have resulted in some mitigation of these distortions, they are likely to continue as long as the monetary conditions that make MCAs necessary persist. Nevertheless there is still room for British producers and processors to improve their competitivity with imports through greater efficiency.

The stabilizers proposed by the Commission in October 1987 and eventually adopted by the Council with characteristic modifications, cover the whole range of products that are in excessive surplus or account for rising budgetary expenditure, sugar, oilseeds and cereals being those most affecting British farmers. Quotas were the key feature of the CMO for sugar and sugar-beet from the beginning.

Since 1981 what are effectively stabilizers have linked price to the level of output. The price penalties paid by producers, designed to finance the cost of exporting sugar surplus to internal demand proved inadequate to do so, and new measures had to be introduced to pay off the accumulated arrears. Although a special import quota of 1.3 million tonnes is enjoyed by the cane-producing states associated under the Lomé Convention, the Community will come under increasing pressure, especially during the Uruguay Round, to reduce its exports – some two to three million tonnes of beet sugar a year, though not all of it subsidized – in view of their depressing effect on world prices to the detriment of third world producers.

The substantial price incentives to farmers through deficiency payments led to a tripling of budgetary expenditure on oilseeds between 1980 and 1987. Progressive cuts in price support related to the volume of output were accepted by Ministers in a less severe form than proposed by the Commission. The proposed stabilizing mechanism – effectively a consumption tax – on vegetable oils and fats was designed to provide revenue that would partly defray the support costs. Although the Commission claimed that since there would be no discrimination between imported and domestic supplies, the tax would not contravene GATT rules, this view was not shared by third country suppliers of oilseeds, notably the United States soya producers. Like earlier proposals of a similar kind this one was vigorously opposed by northern Member States on the grounds of the increase in food prices to which it would lead. The blocking minority in the Council constituted by Britain, the Netherlands and the FGR eventually prevailed.

The problem of bringing the supply of cereals into closer relation with demand became a major preoccupation of both Commission and Council during the early 1980s. In 1985, following the record 1984 harvest, the Council failed to agree, owing to German opposition, a price cut of even 1.8%. This was already half the rate conceded by the Commission during the price negotiations. In the light of the harvest out-turn, which had exceeded the then production threshold by over 8%, the Commission had originally proposed the maximum price cut of 5% fixed the previous year by the council itself for exceeding the threshold. In deference to continuing German pressure the Commission proposed in 1986 to substitute for the threshold arrangement a 'coresponsibility levy' or production tax on the lines of the levy imposed on milk producers since 1977. This was fixed at 3% of the intervention price on all sales of cereals off farm. Since sales between farms were, for administrative reasons, excluded and 'small' producers are eligible for reimbursement of the levy on up to 25 tonnes, the deterrent effect of the levy on the output of cereals and the benefit to FEOGA were both much reduced. Nor, as British opposition to the levy stressed, did it have the beneficial effect on demand to be expected from a straight price cut. Anticipating that, *ceteris paribus*, the Community's intervention stocks of cereals might, failing more effective disincentives to production, reach over 90 million tonnes by 1992, the Commission returned in its 1987 stabilizer package to the concept of a production threshold. This would be set at 155 million tonnes (average cereal production in EC-12 from 1984 to 1986 being 161 million tonnes), and would be combined with stringent seasonal limitations to intervention buying. The price penalties attached to the production threshold would be applicable during the year immediately following the harvest instead of in the following harvest year. This proposal again met with the uncompromising opposition to price cuts of the German Minister of Agriculture, who gave enthusiastic support to the alternative concept of giving financial inducements to farmers to take land out of production ('set-aside'), the result of a compromise reached by the special European summit in February 1988. The threshold was eventually set at 160 million tonnes. The 3% price cut that will penalize any excess will be applied in the following harvest year and not immediately in the current year as proposed by the Commission. Although a 3% increase in the co-responsibility levy is to be applied, it will be reimbursed should the threshold not be exceeded.

Common financing

At this point it is appropriate to consider the future stability of the CAP's third so-called pillar, common financing. The perennial wrangle over Britain's net contribution to the budget and the appropriateness of 'burden sharing' has effectively related to agricultural spending. The year to year rebates conceded to Britain from 1979 onwards and then consolidated on a semi-permanent basis at Fontainebleau in 1984 were therefore seen by purists, notably the French, as a grave breach of the principle of common financing. It looked like an attempt by Britain to exact from its partners an unacceptable *juste retour* – in the French sense of an exact balance between budget contributions and drawings rather than in the British sense of a fair one.

This apparent breach of principle has nevertheless enjoyed the sympathetic connivance of the Council and the other Member States. On the other hand all independent direct national aids to agriculture, which necessarily sidestep common financing, have to be notified to the Commission – an obligation that is not always punctiliously observed – and are subject to scrutiny under the Community's rules of competition. Persistence in maintaining so-called non-compatible aids – essentially those which give additional price support to products subject to a CMO – may lead to proceedings in the European Court of Justice. The most important legitimate departure from strictly common financing has concerned expenditure from the Guidance Section of FEOGA, where contributions from the Community budget have normally to be complemented by counterpart funds from national treasuries. The projects financed in this way are of a broadly 'structural' kind, generally for improving structures of production, marketing and processing of agricultural produce. Expenditure also relates to aids available to farmers in the Community's extensive less favoured – mainly mountain and hill – areas (LFAs). The Community share of financing may vary between 25 and 70% according to the prosperity of the recipient Member State, with Ireland, the Mediterranean area and Portugal enjoying the highest degree of assistance and Britain being at the lower end of the scale. However, in some cases, particularly where LFAs are concerned, Member States enjoy considerable discretion as to the extent to which Community funds may be topped up, to a maximum prescribed level, out of national treasuries, or even in some cases financed exclusively by them. The nearest which these structural aids come to directly assisting production are the so-called compensatory allowances, related to the headage of certain types of livestock (pigs and poultry being excluded) that compensate producers in LFAs for the topographical and other dis-advantages of farming in remote and hilly country.

Unfortunately, as the history of the original structural directives showed, a Member State such as Italy whose agriculture is particularly in need of structural improvement, has lacked the administrative and fiscal resources to take full advantage of them. British governments, on the other hand, even though obliged to provide the necessary counterpart funds, have accepted that grants from the Guidance Section of FEOGA are one of the limited ways in which Britain could obtain a positive financial benefit from the CAP. They are likely to continue to take this view, especially as regards remoter areas where farmers are less capable of coping with the downward pressure of stabilizers on market support prices.

In 1985 the British government took the initiative in persuading its partners to include in the new structural regulation authority for Member States to pay compensation, albeit without the financial participation of the Community, to farmers for the loss of income involved in undertaking schemes for the conservation of the national environment. By 1987, however, a major revision of the regulation included provision for Guidance Section finance towards an annual premium per hectare to compensate the loss of income to farmers who 'introduce or maintain for at least five years, farming practices compatible with . . . the protection of the environment and of natural resources or . . . the maintenance of the landscape and the countryside' (Commission, 1987b). This confirmed the policy initiated by the British government the previous year of establishing environmentally sensitive areas within which farmers could receive this type of compensation. Another innovation also followed closely a British initiative of making grants for the establishment of farm woodlands. The regulation was innovatory inasmuch as all the measures were motivated by the need to reduce farm output and particularly that of surplus products. Compensation was to be made available to farmers who reduced the intensity of the production – initially of cereals and beef – so as to reduce it by at least 20%. Besides this so-called 'extensification' there was also provision for 'conversion' of production of surplus products to crops not in surplus (Commission, 1987b). For the first time extensification provides scope for aiding those who convert their holdings into organic farming. Member States, which are in any case required to contribute a share – in the case of the prosperous ones a major share – of the compensation costs, are given considerable discretion in applying the amended regulation.

The structural measure that will mark the most radical departure yet from the tradition of the CAP also derives from a British initiative. Although 'set-aside' is of longstanding transatlantic origin, its introduction into the Community as a contribution to solving the problem of cereal surpluses was first proposed in a paper circulated by Michael Jopling to his colleagues in the Agriculture Council in 1986. At about the same time an experimental scheme was being launched in Lower Saxony. In setting a minimum on each holding of 30% of arable land to be fallowed, for at least five years, the Commission has estimated that a Community set-aside scheme – obligatory on Member States but optional for their farmers – could result in up to 1 million ha being taken out of use, involving a reduction of some 3.5 million tonnes of grain or about 2% of the Community's annual output. At the level of compensation being proposed the scheme seems unlikely to be attractive to specialist cereal growers on the best land, particularly those with high fixed costs. Although initially for a five-year period, set-aside, if it has any appreciable effect on inhibiting the growth of cereal output, is likely to become at least a semi-permanent instrument of policy.

According to the EC Commission, in the scheme's first year (1988/89) some 430,000 ha in nine Member States were set-aside. This comprises less than 1% of the Community's total arable area. Delays in setting up the necessary administration and poor publicity for the scheme are said to be the main reasons, and at least a similar response is hoped for in 1989/90. But even if it rises to one million ha (or 1.5% of the arable area) the consequent reductions in output, which will come mainly from the more marginal types of land, is unlikely fully to compensate for the normal increase in yields from the better land remaining in production.

A recent independent report to the Commission examined the implications for output of crop and livestock production in the Community of a wide range of biotechnologies (Bureau Européen de Recherches, 1988). (Bovine and porcine somatropin, over whose licensing there lies a large political question mark, were specifically excluded.) Many of those considered will be commercially available from at least 1995 onwards, and are expected to have been widely adopted within the following decade (see Chapter 3). For instance, DNA/MAB diagnostic probes, assisting the early detection of disease, and the use of viral vaccines (peptides or dead antigens) could between them increase the productive potential of pigs, dairy and beef cattle by over 11%.

In the case of crops the effects on yields arise mainly from the introduction of probes for early disease detection; the transformation of crops
with genes for viral components; broad spectrum herbicide resistance,
simplifying weed control; and the introduction of pest-combatting genetic
characteristics. The authors estimate that DNA/MAB probes, taking
account of the likely extent of their adoption, could lead to an average
increase in production of the principal arable crops in the Community of
between 6 and 8% by 2005. The likely increases in production resulting
from other technologies range from 6 to 12%. Owing to overlap the total
impact will of course be less than the sum of individual impacts.

Given a continuing need for constraints on total output, whether for
budgetary reasons or through constriction of internal and external demand,
or both, these developments in biotechnology are bound to lead to a further
decrease in the area required for crop and livestock production in the
Community as a whole. Britain's relatively favourable production structures may lead to a proportionately greater decrease in area there than in
some other Member States.

The potential increase in the production of cereals (and of complementary oilseed crops) continues to confront the Community with the
gravest threat to the stability of the CAP since the introduction of quotas
called a halt to mounting surpluses of milk. A majority of cereal growers in
Britain will remain in business, provided they are not carrying a heavy
burden of capital debt, at the lowest level of cereal price support that is
likely to be politically acceptable to the Council of Ministers. But if price
cuts are to be sufficiently stringent to slow down the pace of expansion and
keep expenditure within whatever bounds are required by budgetary
discipline, it may be necessary to provide relief to some farmers, especially
those operating small enterprises in a difficult physical environment.
Agricultural economists have for a number of years been recommending
that direct income aids on a degressive basis should be paid to farmers who
are unable to survive at – or need time to adapt to – the level of price
support calculated to maintain output roughly in balance with demand
(Uri, 1970). The objection of farmers' unions to their members being thus
seen to be receiving public assistance, as well as its potential budgetary
cost, for long carried sufficient political weight with the European Commission to discourage it from proposing an expedient that would attempt to
reconcile the economic and fiscal advantages of price cuts with their
possibly harmful social effects. In any case the Commission knew with
certainty from long experience that the market clearing price level
envisaged by economists would never be accepted by the Council.
However, as a complement to the wide range of stringent price penalties
contained in its 1987 stabilizer package, the Commission proposed the
introduction on a Community basis of direct income aids for farmers who
either needed short-term help to adapt to the lower level of price support
or a supplement to their income until retirement if they were unable to do

so. In the first case the scheme would be partly financed by the Community. In the second, Member States would be free to set up national schemes. These must comply with common criteria designed to avoid the evident risk that the aids would simply be diverted into increasing output, not only of cereals but of the other products which the stabilizers were designed to limit (Commission, 1987a). The scheme, which is optional, is not applied in Britain, which, during the Council debates, opposed its introduction.

As a result of the watering down of the stabilizer programme under the irresistible pressure on the Commission of all but the British and Dutch Ministers of Agriculture, there can be no certainty that the price penalties eventually agreed will be sufficient to counteract the effect on output of a continuing steady rise in yields of cereals. Commission and Ministers will continue to explore all possible means of avoiding the only measure which proved effective in stemming ever-increasing yields of milk. If, as the result of static internal demand and a gradual shrinking of the world market for grains – not certain but quite possible – the Community finds itself with stocks that can only be disposed of at mounting budgetary cost, quotas may become inevitable. The administrative inconvenience of a very much larger number of points of first sale, including intra-farm sales, than in the case of milk and sugar would make it necessary to set quotas on an acreage rather than a quantitative basis. However, the operation of set-aside will by then have helped to create the necessary administrative structures that might not previously have existed in some Member States. Restrictions on oilseeds, an essential complement to cereal quotas, could, on the other hand, be applied quantitatively at the limited number of crushing plants.

Before this ultimate step has to be taken, however, every effort will have been made to find other means of disposing of surplus cereals, including non-food uses, which may also absorb other products in actual or potential surplus, or of converting cereal land to the production of alternative crops that are in greater demand. In most cases this will only be achieved by means of a subsidy to bridge the gap – even if a gradually narrowing one – between the price at which an industry is obliged to pay for such raw materials within the Community and the price at which its competitors outside the Community are able to purchase them on the world market. The starch industry's subsidized uptake of cereals for non-food uses seems to be close to its limit. The capacity of the starch and chemical industries to absorb sugar is potentially much greater. They also have some potential demand for vegetable oils and fats and for a number of specialized medicinal plants. There is too some scope for a larger output of natural fibres for the textile and cordage industries. But the demand for these commodities is limited and apart from having to be subsidized they must meet competition from alternative synthetic raw materials. Both these factors are highlighted in any assessment of the merits of using cereals and sugar on a large scale as a feedstock for bio-ethanol. At any foreseeable level of the oil price the rate of raw material subsidy required to support its production as a substitute for oxygenates based on fossil fuels would be prohibitive, and much higher than current levels of refund payable on exports of surplus cereals and sugar (Neville-Rolfe and Caspari, 1987).

Whatever future shocks disturb the stability of the CAP's three pillars, the revolution in British agricultural policy which was completed by the end of the transitional period in 1977 will not now be reversed. Farmers' receipts from the market will continue to fluctuate between an upper limit set by threshold prices and a lower limit that will not necessarily be guaranteed by intervention prices. Thanks to international pressures on the one side and budgetary ones on the other, both will be incline to follow a downward trend in real terms, and will in some cases suffer nominal cuts as well. So long as sterling remains weak relative to the basket of EMS currencies and floats outside the European Exchange Rate Mechanism (ERM), farmers will also suffer the penalty of fluctuating MCAs and an undervalued green pound, and British governments will continue jealously to preserve their residual leverage over national prices. At the same time a gradual shift in the emphasis of Community policy from market price support alone to structural measures will provide governments with some additional scope for taking autonomous decisions.

Some current issues

The Commission's proclaimed aim is to abolish the MCA system by 1992, to coincide with the planned completion of a single internal market. Abolition of all intervention buying would achieve this aim, since the existence of MCAs results from differences in intervention prices, as denominated in national currencies, paid in each Member State. But however much the conditions for intervention continue to be circumscribed, complete elimination of this key feature of the CAP appears unlikely.

Logically, too, the single market will be incomplete without the existence of a common currency, which would effectively eliminate the need for MCAs. Not only does this seem a rather remote possibility, but it is even doubtful whether all the other components of a true common market will be in place by the target date.

However, in the meantime a British government will almost certainly have taken the decision to participate in the ERM. In that case the MCAs will be fixed, or at least fluctuate within narrower limits (as have the Italian and Spanish MCAs since those countries joined the ERM in 1980 and 1989 respectively), to the general benefit of British farmers. Moreover, despite all the political, economic and monetary obstacles, it cannot be excluded that at some point before the end of the century, completely free movement of agricultural produce and foodstuffs will become a reality from which British agriculture should be well equipped to take advantage.

The advantage will continue to lie largely in its relatively sound structure, in the greater scope this has tended to provide over the years for adopting innovations in arable and livestock husbandry, and, if to a lesser extent, in marketing techniques. Therefore, if the system of production stabilizers is to be firmly applied and budgetary discipline strictly enforced, in the continuing cost/price squeeze which must result the British should enjoy some comparative advantage in adapting to change, bearing in mind the generally less well structured agriculture of the other Member States. The ability of milk producers to maintain gross margins in the face of quotas has provided one example. Most specialist cereal growers are likely to find ways of adapting to lower cereal prices, or even to quotas; and as innovations resulting from biotechnological research become available during the last years of the century, many British producers should be able rapidly to adopt them.

Nevertheless there will be many farmers in all Member States, including Britain, who will have difficulty in surviving in a less accommodating economic and political climate. This will be to a considerable extent a regional problem. It will also be a social and environmental one.

Since all Member States will be affected, common measures will have to be found to help resolve these problems. As such measures will be financed out of the so-called structural funds – the Regional Development Fund, the Social Fund and the Guidance Section of FEOGA – national governments will be required to contribute to their cost.

For a British government this will have two implications. In the first place it will enjoy a certain freedom of choice in the way in which the structural measures are applied and in the level of its contribution, in contrast to the strict and uniform application of the market regulation which Member States are required to follow. In the case of grants from the Regional Fund, for instance, British governments have generally chosen to ignore the principle of 'additionality', so that Community funding has simply replaced equivalent national funding and not supplemented it.

On the other hand, a British government will be required to find a larger share of financing any measures (especially where aid from FEOGA is concerned) than will be required of those of its partners who are less prosperous. The North–South dichotomy will be accentuated by the decision taken at the 1988 Brussels summit that the Mediterranean Member States and Ireland should receive a major share of the enlarged Regional and Social Funds. This decision means that there will be further positive discrimination in favour of the poorest rural areas of the Community and their farming population.

In its regional aspects, Community policy is likely to concentrate on preventing the rural depopulation which, some member governments believe, could be accentuated by measures, such as set-aside and 'extensification', designed to check the growth of output. This policy would include the encouragement of tourism and local craft industries and the establishment of new light industries in the countryside. These would provide additional sources of income for farmers and their families, and would lead to a still wider spread of part-time farming as a solution to the problem of low incomes in agriculture.

Any Community system of direct income aids to compensate for the lower level of price support made necessary by budgetary discipline or new commitments in the GATT will be designed essentially to help those farmers least well endowed with resources of land and capital. Those with well-structured holdings will be expected to absorb price cuts through improved efficiency and higher productivity.

Definition of the dividing line between these two categories of farmers – those needing direct income support and those who can manage without it – is likely to be left largely to the discretion of Member States. In the British case, should a future government opt for applying the Regulation, not only will the minority of farmers entitled to such assistance be smaller than elsewhere, but the rules for entitlement may well be stricter, in that recipients' total income, and possibly that of their whole household, may be taken into account rather than their farm income alone.

During the early 1980s the protection of the environment became a matter of particular concern in Britain, largely as a result of the very success of its well-structured agriculture in achieving economies of scale and adopting modern intensive production methods. In the case of effluent disposal from livestock enterprises, the principle that 'the polluter pays' can be effectively enforced, since the polluter is readily identifiable. The build-up of nitrates in groundwater or watercourses cannot be ascribed with similar certainty to individual arable or grassland farmers who use heavy applications of nitrogen, or indeed be ascribed exclusively to farmers at all.

The failure of the British government to apply within the prescribed period of grace the 1975 Directive establishing maximum levels of nitrates in drinking water (Commission, 1975b) led the Commission to institute proceedings against Britain in the European Court of Justice. It seems likely, therefore, that the British government will be obliged, at least in certain areas, to take control measures similar to those being applied in other Member States, notably Denmark and the Netherlands, where agriculture is so far the predominant activity that this type of pollution can plausibly be laid at its door. A draft Community Directive along these lines (Commission, 1988b) prescribes maximum quantities of animal manures to be spread on the land. Rules would have to be established on the timing and method of application, and on the capacity of storage facilities. Rates of application of chemical fertilizers would take into account the different rates at which crops take up nitrogen from the soil, including that which has resulted from the application of organic manures. Adoption of these proposals would present considerable problems of policing, but there will clearly be strong pressure from Member States already applying such measures for any common criteria to be no less restrictive than their own.

Originally, however, the British government's concern for the environment was more clearly focused on the conservation of flora and fauna and their natural habitats. Consequently, farmers have been enabled to enter into management contracts whereby they are compensated for the imputed income foregone by adopting less-intensive methods of husbandry on or near sites of special scientific interest (SSSIs).

In the more extensive Environmentally Sensitive Areas (ESAs) established since 1987 (Commission, 1987b), a similar kind of arrangement is available. As the acreage needed to satisfy the Community's demand for cereals (including that for export) declines as a result of steadily rising yields, more land is likely to become circumscribed within this type of restriction on the freedom of farmers to do as they like with their land.

Another aspect of the same tendency towards 'sensitive' farming is that it will respond to the growing public demand for food produced organically, and thus less intensively. The economics of this type of production are now being fully explored and there is no doubt that in some conditions it can be profitable as well as being in keeping with the 'green' movement. Just how large the market for organic food will become is a matter for conjecture. For the producers there is a risk that too many will be competing to satisfy a limited demand, and prices will be insufficiently rewarding.

In Britain the Nature Conservancy Council and the Countryside Commission will continue to remind the Agricultural Departments of the strong public concern which began to make itself felt in the early 1980s and has now gained very powerful support from the media. Large numbers of people, and especially schoolchildren, have become very alert to the harmful effects that intensive forms of agriculture may have on the environment.

The importance now attached to environmental issues is a striking demonstration of the shift in public and parliamentary attitudes to agriculture which has taken place since Britain first applied to join the European Community almost 30 years ago. Some issues which dominated the two negotiations for British accession are now virtually dead. In Brussels the annual review of the economic situation of agriculture and the determination of prices never came to resemble the close confrontation between farmers' unions and civil servants which used to occur in Whitehall. COPA's views receive polite attention, but they now have little influence on the Commission's price proposals which, since 1981 at any rate, have been motivated mainly by budgetary considerations. Given the straitjacket within which expenditure on agricultural market support is now supposed to be confined, the reduced influence of producers' views on policy, in Brussels at any rate, will persist for the foreseeable future.

For much the same reason, another live issue has been laid to rest. The minimal increase in institutional prices, combined with rather low rates of general inflation for several years and assisted, it must be said, by rather limited devaluations of the green pound, have largely extinguished the former preoccupation of the British public with the effects of the CAP on food prices. It seems unlikely to be re-awakened unless, for instance, the Commission were to revive its proposal for a tax on vegetable oils and fats.

On the other hand, three issues which were high on the agenda at the time of negotiation for British entry are still very much alive: Britain's contribution to the budget; deficiency payments; and access for third country produce.

The budget issue, which soured relations with Britain's partners for the best part of a decade, was removed from the Community's agenda for a further five years when in 1988 the Heads of Government, meeting at Brussels, renewed the rebate agreed at Fontainebleau in 1984. By 1992 the constraints on price support for 'northern' products and the increased bias of 'structural' expenditure towards the southern Member States are likely to have added some countries, notably France, to the number of net contributors to the budget. Consequently there may well be pressure for compensation to be more widely shared and not be confined to Britain.

The variable premium (deficiency payment) for beef, introduced under pressure from the British and applied only by them, has, after being steadily eroded over time, been abolished. That for lamb is due for abolition by 1992. A deficiency payment for oilseeds was adopted by the Community before Britain's accession, because low rates of import duty bound in the GATT prevented the Six from introducing their more protectionist system of variable levies. It has led to just that open-ended budgetary commitment which the Six foresaw would be multiplied if they adopted the British system over a wide range of products. Indeed, as a consequence of the soaring budgetary cost of the oilseeds regime it has been necessary to apply the sort of price penalties on excessive production with which British farmers became familiar from the late 1950s onwards.

British demands, during both sets of accession negotiations, for greater access for third country produce to the Community's markets were concerned essentially with defending the interests of the Commonwealth. The Lomé protocol will clearly not be rescinded. It might even be extended to accommodate additional imports of cane sugar from states more recently associated with the Community under the Convention. Although the New Zealand butter quota has seemed to be much more at risk in the light of the Community's own dairy quotas and the increased percentage of the declining UK market which even the reduced New Zealand quota represents, it was nevertheless renewed in 1989 for a further three years, declining by 1992 to 55,000 tonnes, exactly a third of the original level of 1973. The accession of Spain and Portugal has increased the Community's self-sufficiency in sheepmeat. The so-called voluntary restraint agreement with New Zealand, which has assured it a generous import quota of lamb since the CMO for sheepmeat was established in 1981, was therefore renegotiated in 1989. To compensate for a 20% cut in volume the quota now enters duty free.

Defence of purely Commonwealth interests will tend to become subsumed in a continuing British concern for freer world trade in the context of the Uruguay Round of multilateral trade negotiations. But the Community negotiates as a single entity. As the controversy over the proposed oils and fats tax made clear, a British government can count on a very limited number of its partners to influence Community policy in the direction of mutual concessions to the other signatories of the GATT. These include in the so-called 'Cairns Group' the members of the 'old' Commonwealth whose long-term access to the Community markets Britain notably failed from the outset to secure.

All parties to the Uruguay Round, including the Community, are committed to securing a greater liberalization of agricultural trade, especially through the reduction of subsidies. Although its principal inter-locutors, the United States and the Cairns Group of 13 mainly exporting countries, envisage the eventual elimination of subsidies, it seems inconceivable that the Community could ever agree to the total demolition of that central pillar of the CAP, 'Community preference', involving as it does the variable import levy and export refund system. Even the conversion of levies, by a process of 'tarification', into equivalent fixed import duties is strenuously resisted. Some levy-free or fixed levy import quotas of cereals could prove acceptable, on the lines of ACP (African Caribbean and Pacific) sugar and New Zealand butter and lamb, but only as a quid pro quo for raising the level of duty on imported cereal 'substitutes' (Economist Intelligence Unit, 1989).

The concept of 'decoupling' measures of market support from those designed to maintain farm incomes in other ways has been widely discussed during the current negotiations. From the Community's point of view the compensatory amounts paid to farmers in LFAs, the set-aside and extensification schemes, compensation paid for adopting more environmentally friendly forms of husbandry, aids to conversion of farm land to woodland, and those encouraging diversification to non-agricultural activities, all represent sources of farm income that are divorced from production. All of them also coincide with the views set out by the Commission in its 1988 discussion paper on the future of rural society (Commission, 1988). There the need is stressed for policies that prevent further rural depopulation, encourage concern for the human and natural environment in the countryside and meet increasing consumer demand for wholesome food.

Increased preoccupation of Member States with food quality and safety is bound to lead to an extension of Community legislation in this field, if only to avoid distortions to competition. Directives on pesticide residues and food additives have been in force for some years, and many of the Commission's proposals for achieving a single European market by 1992 relate to animal and plant health.

The Commission's concern for the future of rural society in all its aspects rather than exclusively from the point of view of the farming population reflects a reinterpretation of the objectives of Article 39 of the Rome Treaty rather than their abandonment. The need to cut support prices and introduce maximum guaranteed quantities represents at least a tacit admission that the CAP has been primarily a social rather than an effective economic policy. Ministers of Agriculture are under pressure from new lobbies unheard of 30 years ago. They have to recognize that the maintenance of the family farm proclaimed in the Stresa declaration of 1958 as a principal aim of the Community's future agricultural policy cannot be divorced from the wider interests of the rural environment and the well-being of the countryside, particularly in the poorer, now predominantly southern, regions. Nevertheless, within these considerable constraints, the three pillars of the CAP – Community preference, common prices and common financing – seem likely, for all the battering they have received over the years, to stand for some time yet, and price support will continue to absorb the major share of Community expenditure on agriculture (Commission, 1988c).

References

Bureau Européen de Recherches SA (1988) *The Impact of Biotechnology on Agriculture in the European Community to the year 2005*, Brussels.

Commission of the European Communities (1975a) *Stocktaking of the Common Agricultural Policy. Communication from the Commission to the Parliament and Council.*

Commission of the European Communities (1975b) Drinking Water Directive (75/440) (OJL 194, 25 May 1975).

Commission of the European Communities (1979) Drinking Water Directive (79/869) (OJL 271, 29 Oct. 1979).

Commission of the European Communities (1985) Structural Regulation (797/85) and amendments (OJL 093, 30 March 1985, OJL 167, 26 June 1987, OJL 106, 27 April 1988).

Commission of the European Communities (1987a) Implementation of Agricultural Stabilisers (COM(87) 452 final).

Commission of the European Communities (1987b) Conversion Regulation (1760/87), amended (1094/88 and 591/89) OJL 167, 26 June 1987).

Commission of the European Communities (1988a) *The Future of Rural Society.* Communication from the Commission to the Parliament and the Council. (COM(88) 371 final).

Commission of the European Communities (1988b) Nitrates proposal. (COM(88) 708 final).

Commission of the European Communities (1988c) Regulation on the task of the Structural Funds (2052/88) (OJL 185, 15 Oct. 1988 and OJL 374, 31 Dec. 1988).

Commission of the European Communities (1989) Income Aids Regulation (1545/89) (OJL 151, 3 June 1989).

Economist Intelligence Unit (1989) *The Future of European Agriculture: Trade, Technology and the Environment.* London.

Neville-Rolfe, E. (1984) *The Politics of Agriculture in the European Community.* Policy Studies Institute, London.

Neville-Rolfe, E. and Caspari, C. (1987) *Potential for change in the use of land in the European Community for non-food purposes up to the year 2000.* Forecasting and Assessment in Science and Technology (FAST). Occasional Paper no. 178

Uri, P. (rapporteur) (1970) *A Future for European Agriculture.* The Atlantic Institute, Paris.

Chapter 11
Conclusions

Denis Britton

Only ten years ago, Sir Frank Engledow (Emeritus Professor of Agriculture in the University of Cambridge) and Leonard Amey (formerly Agricultural Correspondent of *The Times*) edited a book entitled *Britain's Future in Farming*. Their purpose was 'to take the longer view about the effect of what is being done and what should be done with the land of Britain', in a way which could 'serve the enduring general interests of the country'. They had a panel of 13 contributors, and summed up their findings by stating that 'a main thesis of this whole study is that Britain now needs to increase economic agricultural production . . . A reasoned case for agricultural expansion must continue to be pressed widely and with vigour' (Engledow and Amey, 1980).

This provides a striking illustration of the extent to which our transition from a deficit to a surplus situation in the production of basic foods like cereals and milk has transformed the whole perspective of public discussion about farming. No one is now urging a general expansion of agricultural production. The focus has shifted away from the efficiency of farming – which is even seen as being inimical to the environment – to other matters of deeper public concern, especially the conservation of the countryside and the maintenance of a well-balanced and prosperous rural community in a period of agricultural stress and decline. There is now more concern about people (urban as well as rural) and their relationship to the land, and less concern about maximizing the productive capacity of the soil.

In terms of comparison with other industries, agriculture is now perceived to have surrendered its 'uniqueness' – its claim to special consideration when the economic climate gets rough. This does not mean that farmers' incomes will be abruptly deprived of all the support which has been provided, in various ways, for the past 50 years; but it means that the justification of that support has increasingly been called in question as the high cost borne by taxpayers and consumers has soared to unacceptable levels. A firm constraint has now been placed on EC annual budget expenditure on price guarantees, and producers now know several years in advance that overproduction will be penalized in clearly defined ways.

The number of those regarded as eligible for support is also likely to fall, as payments to farmers are progressively 'de-coupled' from the

quantities they produce, and relate more to their perceived impoverish-
ment, whether or not this is a direct consequence of policy adjustments.
The occupancy of an area of agricultural land is no longer seen as
bestowing a right to a state-guaranteed livelihood or a right to a profitable
market for anything of reasonable quality which the occupant chooses to
produce.

Prices of farm products are no longer so prominent as they were on the
agricultural policy agenda – though they remain crucial to farming prosperity or depression. It is now widely recognized, nationally and inter-
nationally, that markets have to be given a fuller rein in performing their
role of bringing supply and effective demand into balance. Voices are now
heard in the Commission calling for positive application of the economist's
yardstick of 'optimum allocation of resources on the basis of comparative
advantage', which should not be perpetually frustrated by the protection of
structural and regional anomalies.

Higher on the agenda now are measures aimed at preventing
imbalance through various kinds of supply control (e.g. quotas, maximum
guaranteed quantities, co-responsibility levies) and alleviating hardship for
those for whom the discipline of the market proves most severe (e.g. direct
income aids, early retirement allowances). A rigorous price policy is to be
pursued, accompanied by measures 'ensuring a fairer share-out of
sacrifices'.

Another change in the agenda arises from the fact that in 1985, 30%
of farmers in the European Community of Ten were supplementing their
farming activity by other gainful activity, on or off the farm; and that in
75% of cases these other gainful activities accounted for more of the
farmer's time than his actual farm work. This has obviously been to some
extent a consequence of the economic pressures on farm production
already mentioned, and has softened their impact. It is therefore regarded
as a sensible extension of 'agricultural' policy to take steps to promote the
conditions under which these non-farming activities of farm families can
flourish. In the language of the European Commission, which is now
addressing itself to 'the future of rural society' (Commission, 1988b) rather
than to the more battle-scarred arena of the future of the CAP, the new
approach to integrated rural development has to be both 'multidisciplinary
and multisectoral'. In the language of Schumacher, they are looking at the
future use of present agricultural resources 'as if people mattered'. It seems
that there is still a hard core of opinion which looks favourably on action to
maintain the numbers of the farming population, and some even go so far
as to say that the greater those numbers the better, on the grounds that the
farming way of life is physically and morally healthy, and that farm families
make a valuable contribution to rural society. Those who take this view
seldom take explicitly into account the lowering of average farm incomes
which must take place if too many families are striving to obtain a reasonable living from a market whose limits are all too evident.

It has been shown in Chapters 1 and 8 how the total farming income in Britain has been falling in real terms, year after year. It is difficult to see how an increase in the number of farmers claiming a share in that 'pool' of income could do anything but reduce their average living standards. Of course, if the expansion in numbers consisted of part-time farmers who could supplement their farming incomes, expansion could then possibly be accompanied by rising living standards. But usually when people speak in favour of 'upholding the position of the family farm' and reversing the trend towards fewer, larger farms, it is not the substitution of part-time for full-time farming which they have in mind.

The European Commission's formulation and re-formulation of its 'structural policy' for agriculture (first elaborated by Mansholt in 1968, then rejected by Member States on the grounds that it wanted to go too fast and too far in the direction of reducing the number of farmers, and now revived in a modified form which is in many respects reminiscent of a British White Paper on this subject published in 1965) does not shrink from accepting the basic premise that too many people are trying to make a living from farming, and that many thousands of holdings are so small and disadvantaged that 'they will never be able to fend for themselves' (Commission, 1988a), although they do much to maintain local community life.

Once it is accepted that, as we have tried to demonstrate in earlier chapters, there is surplus productive capacity in agriculture and that this situation is more likely to be aggravated than otherwise by future technological advances, policy-makers have to face the clear implication that there is a need to transfer resources out of agriculture into other uses – or render them idle. These resources are mainly agricultural population and land. Their transfer has been in progress for the past 40 years, though at a rate which, as far as land is concerned, has been quite incommensurate with the size of the problem now facing us.

Recognizing that it would be inhumane and politically unacceptable to force these transfers by a relentless application of economic pressure until such time as supply and demand were restored to a reasonable balance, the Commission has proposed a number of measures to improve farm structures – which usually means, to bring some small farms up to a size at which they can expect to secure a reasonable livelihood, and enable the rest to disappear, at least as 'main-occupation' farms, without undue hardship to the present occupiers, and to the lasting benefit of the reduced number of future occupiers of the enlarged farms.

Much thought and discussion has gone into the formulation of these structural policies, and by 1988 they appear to have won a fair measure of consent from the Member States. Financial provisions have been made, in the form of grants from the Guidance section of the EAGGF. Their total impact, however, seems unlikely to be very significant, even though the sums of money available as inducements are considerably greater than was the case with earlier Directives concerned with structural improvement. A more likely prospect is that much outmigration from European agriculture in the coming years will take place under economic duress rather than in response to these well-intentioned provisions.

The British situation in regard to structural improvement is unlike that of the other Member States, in that much of the necessary adjustment of farm size to the post-war technological revolution has already taken place. Moreover, we inherited from the nineteenth century a size structure which was altogether more favourable to profitable management in unprotected markets than was the case on the mainland of Europe.

This is not to say that we have no farms in the Commission's 'social problem' category. A glance at any of the annual reports of the Farm Business Survey, which analyses a large number of farm accounts in England and Wales, will show that a disturbing percentage of full-time farms are operating at very low or negative levels of net income. This is not due simply to inefficiency. Many of these farms do not have sufficient basic resources, particularly of land, to attain a level of output which can afford them a decent living. No doubt if former levels of real prices of farm products still prevailed to-day, a proportion of these 'marginal' farms would be lifted to viability; but as we have shown, those prices have gone and it is highly unlikely that they will return, in the absence of some global catastrophe which we cannot contemplate.

The British agricultural situation therefore resembles that of other countries in that many farms are below the 'threshold' size above which viability and survival seem to be reasonably assured. We therefore still face, like the others, a period of structural adjustment; but it is much less daunting in our case, and we are unlikely to be looking for a large share of the EC Guidance funds.

On the other hand, our government has shown signs of being willing to take energetic initiatives in the direction of the promotion of alternative job opportunities in rural areas for the people no longer needed in full-time farming. This will be only gradual in its effects, but the relief which it could afford in a protracted period of agricultural depression could be substantial, and of lasting benefit.

Apart from measures to assist structural adjustment as a way of relieving the low-income situation on farms, the Commission has given much consideration to another approach, known as direct income aids. This is an embodiment of the principle of 'de-coupling' mentioned earlier. It seeks to support farm incomes in certain circumstances in a way which is not proportional to their production – as is the case with a price guarantee or a livestock headage payment – but which is related to the financial situation of individual farmers or farm households. It envisages a rigorous price policy which will reduce farm incomes at all points on the size-scale, but provides for selective compensation, in the form of cash payments, to those whose livelihood has been most seriously affected by the application of the price policy. Thus all farmers would lose some degree of protection, but some would be compensated for that loss, to a greater or lesser degree.

This form of assistance is not intended to be perpetual, but transitional. It would not extend to the successors of the present occupiers of farms. Unlike structural policy, it is not aimed at the root of the low-income problem in agriculture; but it is intended to ensure support during a period of adjustment, for those farmers in the weakest position financially and socially. It is a helping hand to the 'marginalized' farmer; but will he then be able to stay above the margin and survive without further aid?

It is not at all clear what kind of 'adjustments' the recipient farmers would be expected to make during the limited period of eligibility for income aid, or how those adjustments could be expected to ensure for them a level of farm income which would render unnecessary any further support. Clarification of these matters will be of vital importance if the scheme is to have any chance of attaining its objectives, and not inhibit needed structural change.

Such a scheme will not, of course, be popular with farmers who have large, well-structured and well-equipped farms. Together they account for a large part of total agricultural production, but they will have to bear the full brunt of price reductions and supply controls, without compensation.

Ability to survive is going to be closely linked to ability to compete. The tablets on which fundamental agricultural policy principles are inscribed, notably Article 39 of the Treaty of Rome and the UK Agriculture Act of 1947, appear unimpeachable, but they suppressed an unwelcome paradox. They handsomely avowed the need to give farming people proper remuneration and to ensure a fair standard of living for the agricultural community, but they never made it clear that this undertaking could not realistically extend to all the people engaged in agriculture at any particular time, let alone to all their successors. Because of the finite limits to market capacity to absorb whatever farmers might produce, the industry is highly competitive; and that being so, the weak will go to the wall. The British farmer's main competitor is not the small farmer in France or Germany who labours under structural disadvantages, but his own near neighbour who is planning to enlarge the scale of his operations.

A sound policy for British agriculture should therefore make provision to deal creatively with the expectation of a continuing shrinkage in the number of full-time farmers. This need not involve the exodus of those farmers from the rural communities to which they belong. Nor does it imply the widely deplored 'disappearance of the family farm'. No doubt there will be fewer family farms than in the past, but they will be better adapted to make good use of technological innovations, and will be by far the most numerous type of farm business for a long time to come.

The other major resource which has to be transferred from agricultural to other uses is land. This is a situation which is much less familiar to us than the unceasing movement of farm people to other occupations, and it will be clear from our earlier chapters that there is much uncertainty about the future pattern of land use. The following are some of the questions which have to be put on the agenda for discussion at all levels – local, national and even international.

1. What is the role of the government in shaping the future pattern? Will it need to exercise controls over the use, if any, which is to be made of land taken out of agriculture? Will it need to take steps to prevent a widespread reversion to derelict status? If so, how will 'derelict' be defined and in what respects is it undesirable? Who would pay the cost of preventing dereliction? Is the market in land to remain as free as at present, or is it envisaged that in some circumstances the state should have pre-emptive rights, in the interests of environmental conservation and landscape? How far will it be necessary to restrict the private landowner's rights to do what he likes with his property? Does a need for compensation arise? Will some changes of use attract higher rates of compensation, or inducement, than others?

2. What can be done to promote the necessary changes of use, and to ensure as smooth a transition as possible to the new balance of resources which has to be achieved? Is the change of use to be spontaneous and a matter for countless individual decisions by the present and future owners, or is any co-ordinated planning thought to be necessary? How much reliance will be placed on persuasion, financial inducement or coercive direction? Will the pace of change be a matter for public policy, and if so, what targets will be set, and in relation to what time schedule?

3. To what extent should policy provisions be uniform throughout the country, and to what extent should there be discrimination between regions and special local conditions? If public funds are to be devoted to securing a desirable pattern of land use, how far would the government be justified in 'targeting' those funds towards selected areas, and what criteria should be invoked?

4. If farmers do not take up the offers made in the voluntary 'set-aside' scheme, should it be made compulsory? If so, what rates of payment would be appropriate, over what period and on what conditions of upkeep of the land taken out of production?

5. How far can and should the idea of paying farmers to manage their land in an environmentally sensitive manner be pursued? Would it be sensible to give specific help to 'low-input' systems of farming, as a way of reducing production and environmental nuisance?

Most of these questions are already the subject of vigorous debate, and have been forcefully exposed to the public eye and ear through television, the press and radio. Before too long, the discussion period should give way to attempts to reach an informed consensus, on the basis of which countless individual and local transactions can proceed.

We may be able to 'muddle through' without a clear sense of direction; but in bringing about the revolution in land use which now appears to be imposing itself upon us, under the relentless pressure of scientific discovery and its practical application, it would be better to agree first on the elements of a common approach. Perhaps our lengthening experience as Europeans will bring this home to us.

References

Commission of the European Communities (1988a) *The Agricultural Situation in the Community: 1987 Report.*

Commission of the European Communities (1988b) *The Future of Rural Society.* Communication from the Commission to the Parliament and the Council.

Engeldow, F. and Amey, L. (eds) (1980) *Britain's Future in Farming.* Geographical Publications Ltd., Berkhamsted.

Index